B.S.B.I. Conference Reports, Number Eleven

THE FLORA OF A CHANGING BRITAIN

THE FLORA OF A CHANGING BRITAIN

Edited by
F. PERRING

Published for
THE BOTANICAL SOCIETY OF THE BRITISH ISLES
by
E. W. CLASSEY, LTD.
353, HANWORTH ROAD, HAMPTON, MIDDLESEX

Library of Congress Catalogue Card No. 1 SBN O 900848 37 5

Printed in Great Britain at the Pendragon Press, Papworth Everard, Cambridge.

CONTENTS

PREFACE

Although the Conference at which the papers in this volume were originally given took place in 1969, it is most appropriate that they should be published in 1970, European Conservation Year. 1970 is a year in which we have all been asked to consider the future of our environment and the problems which are arising as a result of the increasing pressures on the countryside, pressures which are likely to go on increasing with an expanding and more affluent population creating greater demands for land for industry, agriculture, housing, roads and recreation.

It was with this thought in mind that the Botanical Society of the British Isles decided that at its biennial Conference in 1969 it would look at the main factors which have been altering the British flora, particularly in the twenty-five years since the end of the Second World War, try to assess the trends those changes suggest, and then attempt to predict what may happen to our flora between now and the end of this century. For this purpose they invited experts from a number of disciplines to present papers at sessions concerned with four main areas of change and to consider the effect these may have on our flora: Climate, Land Use, Transport and Chemicals. At a fifth and final session contributors summarised the changes and suggested action for the future.

It might have been expected that such an exercise could have produced a series of papers all predicting a gloomy future for our flora; that this was not so was a credit to the objective way in which the other authors set about their task of looking at the evidence.

On the one hand it is clear that change means that some of our species are rapidly approaching extinction. However, the B.S.B.I., with its widespread network of members who know their local flora intimately, can and must ensure that, by working closely with the national and local conservation organisations, the sites of our rare species are given adequate protection. If this is done no further extinctions need occur.

On the other hand it is equally clear that change can increase the richness of our flora by creating new environments suitable for native species previously of very limited distribution, and for new species introduced from abroad. Thus, on balance, the future flora of Britain could be larger than the flora of the past.

Whatever the changes to our flora which take place between now and the end of the century they will present new problems and fresh challenges to amateur and professional botanist alike. Their researches will now be given an added zest as they find out just how badly wrong were those of us who dared to predict the future in 1970.

Monks Wood Experimental Station,　　　　　　　F. H. PERRING
Huntingdon, June 1970.

CONFERENCE PROGRAMME, 1969   9

held at
**Imperial College of Science and Technology,
South Kensington, London
FRIDAY, 19th SEPTEMBER**

11.00 a.m.   Introduction   Professor C. P. Whittingham,
Professor of Plant Physiology, Imperial College,
London.

SESSION I—CLIMATE

Chairman—Professor C. P. Whittingham.

11.10 a.m.   H. H. Lamb, Meteorological Office, Bracknell.
"Our changing climate".

11.50 a.m.   Dr. J. P. Savidge, Botany Dept., University College,
Aberystwyth.
"Changes in plant distribution following changes in
local climate".

12.25 p.m.   Professor C. D. Pigott, Biology Dept., The University,
Lancaster.
"The response of plants to climate and climatic change".

1.00 p.m. to 2.10 p.m.   Lunch.

SESSION II—LAND USE

Chairman—Professor J. G. Hawkes, Sc.D.,
Mason Professor of Botany, University of
Birmingham.

2.10 p.m.   P. J. O. Trist, O.B.E.,
National Agricultural Advisory Service, Bury St.
Edmunds.
"The changing pattern of Agriculture".

2.50 p.m.   M. Brown, Forestry Commission, Alice Holt.
"The effect of planting trees".

3.20 p.m.   Dr. M. D. Hooper, Nature Conservancy, Monks Wood.
"The botanical importance of our hedgerows".

3.50 p.m.   A. J. Gray, Nature Conservancy, Merlewood.
"The colonisation of estuaries following barrage
building".

4.20 p.m. to 4.50 p.m.   Tea.

SESSION III—TRANSPORT

Chairman—Dr. J. G. Dony, Past President, B.S.B.I.

4.50 p.m.   J. E. Lousley, Past President, B.S.B.I.
"The influence of transport on a changing flora".

5.30 p.m.   A. P. Dunball, Horticultural Advisor, Ministry of
Transport.
"The management and planting of motorway
verges".

6.00 p.m.   Dr. Mary Gillham,
                    University College of South Wales and Monmouth-
                    shire.
                    "Seed dispersal by birds".

7.00 p.m. to 8.15 p.m.   Dinner.

8.15 p.m. to 10.00 p.m.   SOIREE and EXHIBITION MEETING
          in the DEPARTMENT OF BOTANY

SATURDAY, 20th SEPTEMBER

SESSION IV—CHEMICALS
                    Chairman—Professor D. H. Valentine,
                    Professor of Botany, University of Manchester.
11.00 a.m.   Dr. K. Mellanby, C.B.E., Nature Conservancy, Monks
                    Wood.
                    "Our filthy world—the pollution of land, air and
                    water".
11.40 a.m.   J. D. Fryer, Weed research Organisation, Begbroke
                    Hill.
                    "Herbicides and our changing arable weeds".
12.15 p.m.   Dr. H. J. M. Bowen, Chemistry Dept., The University,
                    Reading.
                    "Poison in the air and its effect on our plants".

12.50 p.m. to 2.15 p.m.   Lunch.

SESSION V—PAST AND FUTURE
                    Chairman—E. Milne-Redhead, President, B.S.B.I.,
                    Royal Botanic Gardens, Kew.
2.15 p.m.   Dr. F. H. Perring, Nature Conservancy, Monks Wood.
                    "The last seventy years".
3.00 p.m.   Dr. S. M. Walters, Botany School, Cambridge.
                    "The next twenty-five years".
3.45 p.m.   Summary by the President of the B.S.B.I.

SUNDAY, 21st SEPTEMBER

Excursion to Forestry Commission Forest at Alice Holt,
Bentley, Hampshire led by M. Brown in the morning, followed by a
visit to the Surrey Naturalists' Trust Reserve at Thursley Common
in the afternoon led by R. M. Fry.

OUR CHANGING CLIMATE

H. H. LAMB

Meteorological Office, Bracknell

The continuity of change

Our climate is forever changing. No two successive years are the same. Personal impressions tell us that successive decades are not the same. It can, as a matter of fact, be established that even successive centuries and millennia differ. The mean values of the climatic variables, temperature, rainfall, and so on, over these long periods plainly differ rather more than is statistically to be expected from the year to year variability.

Changes in our climate are due in part to natural causes, but we may now be reaching the stage (in some degree we reached it a long time ago) where Man and his activities are capable of changing the environment not just directly, but also indirectly, through inadvertently affecting the climate.

There are today meteorologists engaged in considering the global circulation, and what affects it, particularly those meteorologists whose bent is towards mathematical models of the atmospheric circulation and the physical conditions which control the behaviour of these models, some of whom, having a social conscience and noting the world's population explosion, argue that Man will not long be able to afford to leave the climate alone. However, our technology is not yet far enough advanced to undertake the greatest schemes for modifying world climate. This is fortunate, because we are a long way short of being able to predict adequately what the consequences of tampering with world climate would be. No climatic pattern that anyone could devise would be an improvement for everybody in all parts of the world. The prospect is alarming, and it is to be hoped that many more years and decades will pass before anyone tries to do anything of this kind.

The greatest changes which have taken place in our landscape and flora since the ice age were caused by changes in climate, at least until Man's intervention in the landscape first became significant. From some time about the beginning of the Neolithic onwards, the changes in the landscape that are indicated by field evidence must be carefully considered as to how far they were due to climate and not to Man. It seems that we shall soon reach, or may now have reached, the stage where Man's acitivity willy-nilly affects the climate more than do the natural causes of fluctuation.

Quite small changes in climate can be important. Changing the summer climate of Britain, for instance, by warming it up by 1°C would give southern England the climate now experienced in northern France, somewhere near the Loire; if the summer climate were cooled by 1°C, southern England would experience climatic

conditions more like those near the Scottish border.   Corresponding
changes in the winter climate are easier to envisage in terms of shifts
from east to west, or vice versa, that is to say towards a more
continental or a more oceanic climate.

FIGURE 1

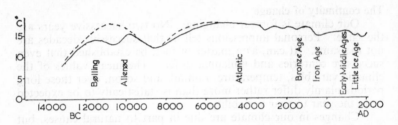

Outline sketch of probable course of the average high summer (July/August)
temperature (°C) in central England, mainly from palaeobotanical results. (Last
1,000 years derived by statistical techniques from historical mss descriptive
records of weather).

Broken line: possible amended course of prevailing high summer temperature
suggested by evidence of beetle fauna.

We have learnt most of what we know of the climatic history
of the British Isles since the ice age from palaeobotany, but recent
evidence from another source seems to indicate that we may have
to modify some of the conclusions to which we have been drawn by
palaeobotany. The work of G. R. Coope of the Department of
Geology in Birmingham University on variations in the insect fauna
of Britain, particularly *Coleoptera* (beetles), suggests that some re-
interpretation may be necessary. Beetles apparently respond more
rapidly to climatic changes than the vegetation does. The curve
(Fig. 1) sketches in outline the most probable course of the changes
of prevailing summer temperatures in central England since the
maximum extent of the last glaciation, as they appear from mainly
botanical evidence. The so-called climatic optimum, i.e. the
warmest period since the ice age, occurred between about 6000 and
3000 BC; it seems to have continued in some degree, though with
some rather wider fluctuations than before, until 1000 BC. Coope's
investigation of the insect fauna, and where the corresponding
species are found today, tends to modify the picture given by the
bold line in Fig. 1 somewhat. In particular, it suggests summer
temperatures getting up to modern values, either in the Bølling
or in Allerød times: it may even entail regarding these two warm
phases as one (as indicated by the broken line in Fig. 1). The
European ice sheet was certainly still present, as we know from other
evidence; so the up and down changes of temperature about those

times might be even more rapid than we have been led to believe. And some of the later changes of climate may have been more abrupt than previously thought also. However, it has to be remembered that the responses of the plant world to a worsening of the climate, i.e. a fall below some tolerance limit of the plants, are likely to be more rapid than their response to an improvement which makes a widening of the area that could be inhabited by the given plant possible. Even birds can be slow to exploit an improvement of climate. In the late 1950s some species of birds were still spreading northwards over Europe and Iceland, and possibly further into the Arctic, although the warmest conditions were already past: in most of Europe and neighbouring parts of the Arctic the years between about 1933 and 1952 were warmer than for decades before that and also warmer than the years since have been.

From somewhere about the Neolithic onwards, Man has so disturbed the landscape in Britain that, if we are to get reliable field evidence of the course of climatic history, we have to turn our attention to other places where Man was not already so destructive of the environment, for instance to places like the Arctic, the higher levels of the Alps, or the Sahara Desert. But for the last 1,000 years or so in Europe there is a great deal of documentary evidence of the behaviour of the climate to be obtained from study of historical sources.

Evidence of climatic variation and its effects

1. *Macroscopic plant remains.* Tree stumps can often be seen in the peat in the Scottish Highlands at a level somewhat above what is believed to be the present-day natural limit of trees. These stumps date from the post-glacial "climatic optimum".
2. *Medieval tillage.* Ridge and furrow, the remains of medieval tillage, go up to about the 1,050 ft contour in Redesdale in Northumberland and over a wide area round about. Nobody—not even in war-time—would think of tilling up to 1,050 ft in Redesdale today, yet this ploughing apparently went on for long enough to affect the form of the ground surface for hundreds of years afterwards. There is documentary evidence of the dates and periods at which this ploughing went on. It continued for 200 years or so until 1250-1300 AD.
3. *Medieval vineyards.* There were many vineyards in England in medieval times, even as far north as Ely and the Fenland. Catherdal records show that the Ely vineyard, like quite a number of others, was kept going for hundreds of years. The owners of these vineyards would hardly have persisted with them, despite a possible willingness to drink rather sourer wine than is nowadays acceptable, if the climatic conditions had been the same as they are today (in particular the frequency of frosts in May damaging the crop). It is true that there are some vineyards in England today, and there have been in most centuries since the Middle Ages, but none of these vineyards has ever outlived the individual enthusiast who established it.

4. *Freezing of the rivers.* For 2 or 3 centuries, from about the year 1540 to 1814, it was not by any means uncommon for the Thames to freeze to such an extent that fairs could be held on the ice in central London. It probably happened in 10 or 12 winters in that time. It would have happened in 1963 but for Man's effect on his environment: the frost in 1963 was more severe, and more prolonged, than the one in 1814 which produced the last frost fair in London; but reliable measurements, which were made near London Bridge at the height of the great freeze of January 1963, showed that the water temperature was around 10°C. That temperature was not achieved by natural means, but by what Man is nowadays doing to the river: the Thames was frozen over, and could be crossed on foot, at Hampton Court, but not below the power stations and factories in Kingston Reach.

5. *Landscape paintings.* The changes of fashion in the treatment of the sky in landscape paintings have been statistically investigated: the changes are found to go hand in hand with the known variations in the prevailing cloudiness of our summers. The summer landscapes of the 17th and 18th centuries painted by Ruysdael and Constable, for example, always show the artists' preoccupation with the clouds. There is very little doubt that the summers were poorer and more disturbed in and around the times when these particular artists lived than the summers of the first half of the 20th century.

Meteorological investigation and understanding of the matter

Fig. 2 shows, mainly by 50-year means, the prevailing temperatures derived from a careful statistical analysis of the abundant manuscript material regarding the behaviour of the climate in England from AD 800 to the first half of the present century. Not surprisingly, there are alternative estimates for the temperatures of the first few hundred years, in the early Middle Ages. Over the year as a whole, for the peak months of summer, the so-called high summer, July and August averaged together, and for the winter three months, December, January and February, we experienced within the first half of this century a warm time, one of the warmest though probably not quite equalling the height or the sustained warmth of a couple of centuries in the early Middle Ages, between 1100 or 1130 and about 1310. The temperature values in the first half of the present century were higher by appreciably more than half a degree Centigrade over the year as a whole, and by more than one degree Centigrade for the winters, than those experienced in the coldest period round about the late 17th century. When one looks at curves of this kind, one has to realize that the whole population of the temperatures goes up and down with the mean values. The extremes occurring are also affected, and the frequency of spells of frost or of great heat etc. goes up or down with the average temperature values.

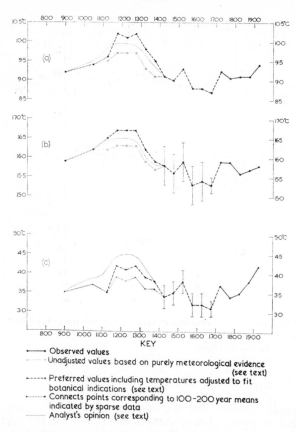

KEY
→ Observed values
······ Unadjusted values based on purely meteorological evidence
(see text)
-----→ Preferred values including temperatures adjusted to fit
botanical indications (see text)
·········· Connects points corresponding to 100-200 year means
indicated by sparse data
——— Analyst's opinion (see text)

Temperatures (°C) prevailing in central England since AD 800, 50-year averages:
   (a) Year
   (b) High summer (July/August)
   (c) Winter (December, January and February).

Observed values (as standardized by Manley) from 1680. Values for earlier periods derived by statistical study of the frequency of various weather phenomena. The ranges indicated by the vertical bars are ± 3 times the standard error of the estimates.

    Fig. 3 takes a closer look at the air temperatures in central England back to about the year 1500: the smooth curves are running 100-year means and the dots are the average values for the individual decades. The peak of warmth in the 1900-1950 period is clearly shown, and our average winter temperatures in the 1960s have come down by nearly 1°C from that peak. The summer temperature values have fallen too: the 1960-1969 July/August average for central England is three quarters of a degree below that of the previous 30 years. Our adaptation to this is quite noticeable:

FIGURE 3

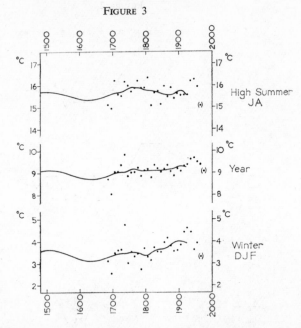

Temperatures (°C) prevailing in central England since AD 1500:
Smooth curves—running 100-year means.
Dots—decade averages,
        from 1680–89
        to   1950–59
        and (bracketed) 1960–65.

most people consider that the summer of 1969 was particularly
lovely, but the average temperature of that summer in the end turned
out to be just equal to the 30-year average for 1931-1960.   Even
so, it was one of the best summers in the decade.   We have become
used to other things besides.   Corresponding to the lower temperatures in the 1960s, the length of the growing season has shortened by
something of the order of 2 weeks.   (It has also effectively shifted
a little later in the year, owing to the continuance of warm Octobers,
at a time when the spring temperatures had been becoming lower
than before.)   Some recent summers in southern England approxi-
mated to the average values for Northumberland in the previous
30 years, though they were not of course so similar to the northern
summers as regards windiness and rainfall.   The over-all average
temperature for the 1960s, averaged over all seasons of the year,
was in fact a return to the over-all average for the hundred years
1851-1950.   The winter temperatures affect the amount of snow
and the frequency with which snow covers the ground.   The
average frequency of snow lying each winter was about 7 days in
typical lowland sites inland in England in the period between the

wars. The average for the 1950s went up to between 10 and 15 days in most places, and in the 1960s the average has been still higher (though largely affected by the one exceptionally long, snowy winter in 1963). Since 1950, then, the average number of days with snow covering the ground in the lowlands in inland districts in England has been roughly double what it was in the inter-war years, and the frequency of occurrence of frosts lasting more or less a whole week (as indicated by the average temperature of each 24 hours being below 0°C) has also risen. The English climate was at about the borderline of occurrence of this, when the winters were as mild as they were in the 1920s and 1930s, when a week of frost was extremely rare. The recent cooling has brought the frequency back to the level that it had in the 19th century, which is about six times what it was in the first half of this century. Cases when the average temperature of a whole month in central England is below the freezing point, and when most of the rivers freeze, as has occurred four or five times since 1940, happened only twice between 1896 and 1939.

The meteorologist must consider how these variations come about. One telling index is the frequency of westerly winds, the winds on which we rely for the well-known maritime, mild, genial

FIGURE 4

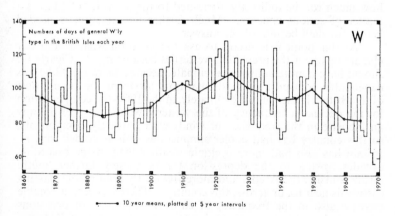

Numbers of days each year from 1861 to 1969 classified as of general westerly type over the British Isles.

(*Westerly type* is defined as pressure high to the south, sometimes also to the southeast and southwest, and low to the north of the British Isles. Sequences of depressions and ridges of high pressure travelling east across the Atlantic and farther east. Weather in the British Isles generally unsettled or changeable, usually with most rain in northern and western districts and brighter weather in the south and east. Winds shifting rapidly between S and NW as each depression passes, sometimes even SE or E for a short time. Cool in summer, mild in winter, with frequent gales.)

nature of the English climate. Fig. 4 shows the number of days a year classified as of general westerly type of weather over most of the British Isles between 1861 and 1968. These are the days when there is a sequence of weather systems coming eastwards across the Atlantic, with their frontal rain belts travelling from west to east across the British Isles, and places with a westward exposure catching the rain whilst there is a certain amount of shelter in eastern districts. We see that in the 1860s there were rather frequent westerlies, although we know that that had not been the case for very long before 1860. That time was near the beginning of about a century of unusually frequent westerly winds and milder weather, which caused a great recession of the glaciers in the Alps and Scandinavia. This unusual frequency of the westerlies, maintained over about a hundred years, resulted in a general warming of the climate in Britain and Europe; and the frequency of westerly winds became very high in the first half of the twentieth century, more particularly between 1900 and the 1930s. Since then there has been a general decline of the westerlies; and 1968, with only 63 days classifiable as of generally westerly type, showed the lowest frequency for any individual year since the beginning of our classification 108 years earlier. There had been several previous years with as few as 68 days of westerly type, but none below that. The total of westerly days for 1969 was 56 days; so something is clearly happening to our climate. How much of the change is due to natural causes and how much can be indirectly attributed to the activities of Man is a matter of serious concern. Much further investigation is needed before we shall be sure of the answer.

At this point it is useful to ask the question what would our climate be like if the prevailing westerlies became rare? Clearly we should have a more continental climate, because there would be less dependable transport of mild, maritime air from the ocean west of the British Isles; but, unfortunately, in the 1960s the compensation for the decline in frequency of the westerly winds has been mainly an increase in the frequency of winds with northerly components, so this country has had cooler summers as well as colder winters. Britain has also had more cyclonic weather than in the preceding decades, owing to the depression tracks passing farther south, farther outside the Arctic, and more frequently than before passing eastwards near to, or across, this country. There has been a notable increase also in the frequency of easterly winds, i.e. of occasions when the depressions are centred even somewhat south of Britain.

These changes in the frequency distribution of winds from different directions naturally affect the rainfall also. Westerly winds, bringing moisture in from the Atlantic, give the hill districts with western exposures their characteristic downpours, whilst inland areas and eastern districts in Britain are somewhat sheltered. With northerly, easterly and southerly, winds the patterns of exposure and shelter are quite different.

Fig. 5 indicates the variations in the prevalence of westerly and south-westerly surface winds in the south-eastern half of England

FIGURE 5

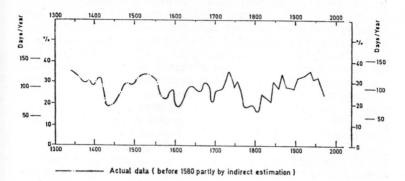

——————— Actual data (before 1580 partly by indirect estimation)

Frequency of SW'ly surface winds in London.
Decade averages from daily weather observations since 1670. Estimated from miscellaneous data in earlier times, including one weather diary in eastern England as early as 1340–43.

since the year 1340. There was a much lower level of frequency before the 1860s than in most of the century that has elapsed since then. Between 1770 and about 1845 we find a number of years and decades with frequencies of these winds as low as those we have experienced in 1968 and 1969. This time was evidently, at least in terms of the winds which generate our climate, rather similar to the climate we are now beginning to experience. The rapidity of the decline of the westerlies around 1750-1770 was also somewhat similar to the change that has occurred since 1950. Something rather similar seems also to have happened 200 years earlier, in the 1560s, and we can even trace the outline of a somewhat similar change once before that, at some unknown time between 1350 and about 1420. We may suspect something in the nature of a repeating 200-year oscillation. Three repeats are, of sourse, far too little to use as a satisfactory, or rather as a satisfying, basis for forecasting. They are certainly too few for us to be certain of what is going on. This fluctuation in the winds, and apparently in the strength of the general wind circulation over the world, may well, however, be related to a variation in the behaviour of the sun which is registered in variations that have been determined by radiocarbon dating laboratories. By proceeding to apply radiocarbon dating methods to material the age of which is already known, it is possible to ascertain the past variations that have occurred in the amount of radioactive carbon in the earth's atmosphere. The variations range over about 2% above and below normal. These variations of radioactive carbon in the atmosphere register something like a 200-year fluctuation that can be traced back over thousands of years, i.e. through many more repeats than just the three cycles of south-westerly wind frequency which we can establish in England.

Thus, we have the beginnings here of something which might lead to a method of forecasting long-term changes of climate.

As the westerly winds gradually recovered in frequency from their low level in the late 18th-early 19th century to their high level of predominance in the early part of the present century, the general total of rainfall over England and Wales rose by about 10%. Since the peak of the westerlies in the early part of this century the rainfall over England and Wales seems to have tended to decline a little, although the decrease of rainfall in the three cooler seasons of the year has been almost made good by an increase in the rain falling in summer. With the decline in frequency of the westerly winds, and the corresponding increases in winds from other quarters, the geographical distribution of the rain falling over the British Isles has also changed somewhat. Places with an eastern or northern exposure have experienced some increase of rainfall; and in 1968-1969 some places with western exposures, in the famous wet regions of the north-west Highlands, had no more than between about 20 and 50% of their former average rainfall.

In a diary kept by Thomas Barker, one of the most devoted and skilful early weather observers, for 40-50 years in Rutland in the mid-18th century, there is a note dated 1775, opining that there had been some sort of change in the nature of the easterly winds in Britain during his lifetime. This note reads "formerly [Barker was here doubtless thinking back to the 1730s and 1740s] we used to associate easterly winds with dryness. Now, we much more frequently get wet easterlies, and they have been associated with some of the heaviest summer rains and with bad instances of flooding". I read this note of Barker's over to a colleague in the long-range weather forecasting branch of the Meteorological Office recently without telling him when it had been written. He thought it an accurate description of the events which we have experienced in our own times and, in particular, of the change from the prevailing dry, and in winter frosty, weather that accompanied easterly winds in the 1930s and 1940s and the slow-moving rains accompanying small cyclonic disturbances over the English Channel and over southern England, which have been prominent in several incidents of serious flooding in 1968 and since.

Some causes of climatic change and the characteristic time-scales of their action

Clearly, some climatic change must take place in the course of the astronomically established variations over tens of thousands of years of the orbit and tilt of the Earth. The general course of the temperature curve which seems to result from these changes is indicated in curve A in Fig. 6 over a total time span which may be of the order of several hundreds of thousands of years. The actual orbital cycles themselves affect the Earth's summer radiation receipt just about enough to vary the temperature over a range of some 2°C. But because this leads to an accumulation of greater amounts of unmelted snow and ice on the land belt in high northern latitudes

FIGURE 6

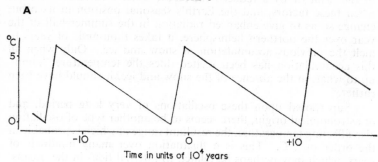

A

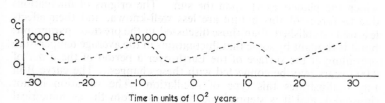

B

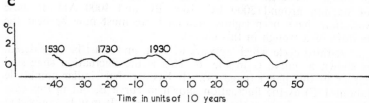

C

Schematic representation (greatly simplified) of three—probably the most important— quasi-periodic variations affecting the surface temperatures prevailing in England,

    (a) Astronomical—cyclic variations of the Earth's orbit etc.
    (b) Tidal force variations
    (c) An apparent 200-year fluctuation possibly originating as a "flickering" of the sun's energy output.

in certain phases of the cycle, and this unmelted snow and ice reflects away and wastes a great deal of the solar radiation, the range of the resulting temperature changes is increased apparently to almost 6°C. Ice ages occur when the radiation received in high northern latitudes in summer is reduced, for instance, by ellipticity of the orbit or by a reduced tilt of the Earth's rotation axis; but when these factors, and the Earth's seasonal position in its orbit, change so as to give enhanced radiation in the summer half of the year over the northern hemisphere, it takes thousands of years to melt the previous accumulation of snow and ice. Only when all this accumulation has been melted does the temperature "jump" up to what, in the absence of the snow and ice, it should have been earlier.

Superposed upon these oscillations of very long period, and of astronomical origin, there seems to be another type of oscillation also affecting temperature, the resultant range of which is probably in the order of 2°C. This is a fluctuation over many hundreds of years, which may perhaps be related to internal tides in the oceans, the amplitude of which changes with the changes in the combined lunar and solar tidal force. There may also be variations of the energy output of the sun itself caused by changes in the tidal force which the planets exert upon the sun. The origins of fluctuations due to forces of this nature are less well-known, and their effects less well established, than those discussed in the previous paragraph; but it is thought by some that fluctuations in the average temperature prevailing at the surface of the Earth over a period of the order of 2,000 years may be connected with these changes. The curve B in Fig. 6 illustrates this type of oscillation. The variation is not sinusoidal, and it is stepped the other way from the asymmetrical step of curve A in Fig. 6. In this case the recoveries are slower, i.e. more gradual, than the declines of temperature; the peaks are at about 2,000-year intervals (possibly corresponding to maxima of warmth around 3000 BC, 1000 BC and 1000 AD—if these variations have been rightly identified, we must now be near the bottom of a trough in this curve).

A third cycle which appears to exist, and must be considered, is shown as curve C in Fig. 6. This is the fluctuation suggested earlier in this paper (page 19). It has a rather similar amplitude (about 1°C) as the fluctuation shown in curve B, but in this case the duration of one cycle is about 200 years. It may be connected with the peaks of warmth in England around 1530, 1730 and 1930. If so, we have now come away from the peak values of warmth of climate around 1930 and are not likely to see a similar level of prevailing temperatures again in our lifetime. This is the only one of the three cycles here mentioned which seems likely to affect climate significantly in our lifetime.

The approach to climatic forecasting

A climatic forecast might be attempted by simply superposing the variations to be expected from continuation into the future of the three cycles of different period lengths here suggested; though preferably such a forecast should only be ventured after a much fuller analysis of the data from the past, and from related scientific evidence outside meteorology, than has yet been made. An awareness of the likely margins of error and the magnitude of short-term fluctuations that would still have to be regarded as of random incidence is also needed. One particular source of random errors needs special mention, namely the possible occurrence, at any time, of very great volcanic eruptions which throw veils of dust high into the atmosphere that persist for several years. The effect of these volcanic dust veils is in general to give a few cooler years in each case, especially the summers being cooler, with average temperatures of the order of 0·5 to 1·0°C below what would otherwise have occurred.

There exists also the possibility of superposed variations due to the activity of Man. Urbanization is already leading to increasing warmth in our towns where most of the population now lives. In the towns we are hardly aware, and our thermometers are hardly aware, of the fall of prevailing winter temperatures since 1930 which has affected the countryside.

There are meteorologists who consider that Man is solely responsible for the climatic changes which have occurred this century. The general warming up to about 1940 was attributed to the increasing concentration of carbon dioxide in the atmosphere as a result of the industrial revolution, and the falling level of temperatures since that time is by these arguments attributed to the dust and smoke and other types of pollution put into the atmosphere by Man's activity now more than compensating the warming effect of the continued, and increasing, output of carbon dioxide. It is observed that the strength of the radiation measured in the direct solar beam on cloudless days has declined by 4 or 5% since the early 1940s: this, it is suggested, could be due to the additional smoke resulting from the industrialization of the less developed countries and to the vapour put into the atmosphere by the exhaust of high-flying aircraft and the rockets with which satellites are launched. However, the fact that rather similar declines of temperature occurred 200 and 400 years ago, long before there were any high-flying aircraft, shows that the present climatic decline may be entirely due to natural causes. Nevertheless, the possibility is a very real one that Man may, with his advanced technology, inadvertently put so many foreign substances into the atmosphere as to tip the climatic balance one way or the other. By greatly increasing the carbon dioxide in the atmosphere, he may warm the world's climate or, by introducing dust and smoke and other substances in greater quantities than before, Man may himself screen off the sun's energy and, in consequence, cool the Earth. Some day in the future, the very multiplication of Man himself, partly by multiplying in size the urban areas and partly by the output of body heat, could also change the climate in the direction of ever-increasing warmth.

Any scientifically based climatic forecast which it may in future be possible to make must be subject to some margin of error due to unpredictable elements of the kinds here mentioned.

DISCUSSION

PROF. J. G. HAWKES asked whether there is an eleven-year climatic cycle.

MR LAMB replied that whilst there is an eleven-year solar cycle there is little evidence for a meteorological one: multiples and sub-multiples are more important: maxima of westerly winds tend to occur at 5½ year intervals.

MR E. MILNE-REDHEAD asked where the moisture brought in by our east winds comes from.

MR LAMB replied that this came from the Baltic and the North Sea. When westerly winds prevailed the effect of the North Sea could be shown by comparing the low rainfall in eastern England with the considerably higher rainfall in Holland. Values as low as those found between Southend and Cambridge did not occur again until as far east in Europe as Berlin.

CHANGES IN PLANT DISTRIBUTION FOLLOWING CHANGES IN LOCAL CLIMATE

J. P. SAVIDGE

University College of Wales, Aberystwyth

Causes of change

An examination of Godwin (1956) and the numerous papers written during the past three decades on pollen stratigraphy of peat deposits reveals that the composition of the flora in any one area has been in a state of continual change over the last 10,000 years. In the past these changes in vegetation were mainly due to the relatively slight changes in climate; but during the last few thousand years man has had an increasing influence on the distribution and abundance of species. The changes in climate have not only affected the environment above ground level, but have also resulted in marked alterations in the structure and mineral content of the soil. The loss of several species which require a base-rich soil, with good drainage, from western parts of Britain during the last few thousand years is the result of the higher rainfall totals and cooler climate of these areas leading to the leaching of minerals and the gradual accumulation of organic matter which makes the soils more acidic and waterlogged.

The effects of climate can be readily observed on mountains and hills where the warmer, drier southern slopes are characterised by good quality hill grazing pastures containing *Agrostis tenuis, A. canina, Festuca ovina, Galium saxatile* and frequently *Pteridium aquilinum;* whereas the cooler, moister and more peaty soils of the northern slopes are covered by heaths *(Calluna vulgaris, Erica tetralix, Vaccinium myrtillus), Carex binervis, Luzula campestris, Nardus stricta, Sieglingia decumbens,* and numerous mosses and lichens. Other environmental factors may also be involved as when we find additional species such as *Plantago lanceolata, Thymus drucei, Trifolium repens, Veronica officinalis* and *Viola riviniana* which will only occur on the more mineral rich soils. Some of the differences are reinforced by selective grazing of domestic and wild animals. Farmers take advantage of these climatic differences associated with aspect: a short journey through hill country will soon show that the more productive and improved fields are on south-facing slopes.

Other obvious ways in which the climate determines the distribution of species can be seen by looking at the maps in the *Atlas of the British Flora*. Species, such as *Cirsium eriophorum, Galium pumilum* and *Tamus communis* are confined to the warmer, drier localities of England and Wales, while, at the other extreme, in the cooler, moister sites at high elevations in north-west Scotland we find the only localities for *Juncus trifidus, Luzula spicata, Veronica alpina* and a number of other species. The first group includes those continental species that are at their northern limit of distribution, while the second group contains those that are at their southernmost stations. The species of these two contrasting groups have, during the course of their evolution, become adapted to very different environmental conditions and will normally only thrive, flower and fruit providing certain environmental factors are present.

A few species appear to be particularly good indicators of climatic change, an example being *Nardus stricta* which is the dominant grass in areas adjacent to permanent and temporary snow-beds. In fact, it is such a good indicator species that Green (1968) and others have used it as a guide to areas where one can expect snow to persist for the greater part of the year in Scotland. These areas of quasi-permanent snow-beds in parts of Scotland appear to be on the increase (Spink 1968, 1969) and could well have a more pronounced effect on the vegetation of these regions if the climate continues to become cooler and moister.

The changes in climate outlined by Lamb (p. 11) will certainly lead to changes in the distribution of species in the British flora, but these changes will affect different species in differing ways. In considering these changes it is vitally important to consider certain genetical and evolutionary implications.

The response to change

Every species has its own range of tolerance to environmental factors—some grow almost anywhere; others are restricted to just one or a few localities. Generally speaking, those species which are widespread (weeds excluded) are outbreeding and possess a considerable amount of genetic diversity, whereas rare species are invariably inbreeding, frequently apomictic, as in *Hieracium,* and have a limited degree of genetic variability. Because their populations are virtually isolated there is no gene exchange between them as occurs in closely adjacent populations of more common species. It is these rare species, with little or no genetic diversity, that are most likely to become extinct if there are marked climatic changes, especially alterations in the local environment.

Some of the rarer species could benefit from certain climatic changes. For instance, if the British climate becomes cooler, wetter, and more humid as suggested by Lamb, a number of arctic-alpine species may extend their range, providing that soil conditions are suitable in adjacent areas. However his suggestion that dry easterly winds may become more frequent could result in some species, which require a continual high humidity, becoming less abundant as a result of occasional periods of desiccation. Continental species which require a warm soil, with a temperature of at least 12°C. for germination, and high summer and autumn temperatures for seed ripening, may well become extinct if the climate becomes cooler and the growing season shorter unless they can adapt themselves to the new conditions.

On the other hand, widespread species are not so likely to be affected by changes in climate since they usually have the ability to undergo genetic change as a result of natural selection. This has been clearly shown by the work of Clausen, Keck, and Hiesey (1940 *et seq.*) in the United States who have worked on variation within and between populations and races of *Potentilla* spp. and *Achillea* spp., and by Bradshaw (1960) and his colleagues in this country who have been looking at species of *Agrostis*. In *Agrostis*, and also in *Silene maritima*, there are considerable morphological and physiological differences between populations within a relatively short distance of one another and, in many instances, it can be shown that these differences are brought about by the selection of certain character combinations for specific sets of environmental parameters.

Most of us are concerned with changes in plant distribution within our own county, region, or locality rather than overall changes in distribution throughout the British Isles. By knowing our local climate we shall eventually obtain a better understanding of how important climate is, both directly and indirectly, in determining the composition of the vegetation within relatively small areas as well as throughout the whole of the area under investigation. Areas with a diverse topography are particularly good for studies of local climate. Investigations will show how the local climate is affected by aspect, angle of slope, and altitude and that for example some species only occur on warm well drained south-facing slopes while others are restricted to cooler and moister north-facing slopes.

Extremes of climate are also important and every opportunity should be taken to find out the consequences of extremes on less common species, especially those that are at the limits of their range. For example, the severe winter of 1962–3 killed over 60% of gorse bushes (*Ulex europaeus*) in lowland parts of mid Wales and most of those that survived died back almost to the base. Some of these eventually recovered, but most of the more vigorous bushes in 1969 were those that had germinated since 1963. This shows that the distribution of *Ulex europaeus* is partly determined by temperature and that it cannot stand severe prolonged cold spells: for this reason it rarely occurs above 150m and then only on south-facing slopes.

For *Ulex europaeus* a single cold winter was not sufficient to cause extinction; but a succession of cold winters could have had a disastrous effect on the distribution of this species, although since gorse seeds appear to survive in the ground for many years it could extend its range again if the winters became less severe. Two points arise from this case: first, the survival of a species partly depends on how long its seeds remain viable; secondly, it is concurrent extremes that can result in a species becoming extinct.

This is where the local observer is at a great advantage since the same extreme climatic events rarely occur throughout the whole of the British Isles. For example, during the summers of both 1968 and 1969 a number of species have wilted and become completely desiccated on shallow Powys-type soils in west Wales where we have had rainfall totals of only about 40% of average; but in eastern England such observations could not be made since rainfall totals have been well above average in each of these two summers.

So far I have avoided giving examples of species which have become either much rarer or more abundant throughout Britain within recent years as a result of climatic change. This is because it is difficult to be sure if any marked changes in distribution *are* primarily due to the gradual changes that have occurred in our climate over the last few hundred years. One might, for instance, think that the occurrence for the first time during the present century of the many hundred of alien species, of a continental distribution type, in southern Britain could be because our winters have become much milder since the middle of the 18th century. These aliens certainly grow more successfully in hot, dry summers and may overwinter in mild winters, but their presence in Britain is more the result of human influence than climatic change. Again, the disappearance of species such as *Agrostemma githago* and *Chrysanthemum segetum* is unlikely to be due to climatic change, but rather to improved seed cleaning techniques and agricultural practices.

Climatic changes have certainly resulted in changes in the distribution of plants in the past and the process is continuing. The most satisfactory way of finding out how important climatic changes are, compared to changes in other environmental factors, in altering the range of a species, is to carry out detailed recording at the same site, especially one at which changes are suspected to occur, at regular intervals. The records should include details on the performance of the species, the time they come into flower, the amount of good seeds produced each year, and how many new plants are added to the population each year. The value of this type of study is very well illustrated in Pigott's paper (p. 32). This information will enable us to build up an environmental spectrum for each species which should tell us the main factors involved in determining the distribution of each species and, finally, to see if certain populations can become adapted to a new range of environmental tolerance rather than become extinct.

The environmental spectrum

In Wales we are trying to produce an environmental spectrum for each species by means of our '00' survey in which we are making a detailed record of the performance of species in the one kilometre square (the '00' square) at the bottom left-hand corner of each of the 10km national grid squares. Recently we have also been looking at other representative 1km squares in order to obtain a fuller coverage. This has provided us with information on the range of tolerance for all but the rare species and by resampling, say at ten yearly intervals, we hope to record changes in distribution and to relate these modifications to climatic factors, changes in land-use, etc.

In areas of diverse topography, like most of Wales, there can be considerable environmental variations within a 1km square and a smaller sampling area is necessary to be sure of arriving at genuine conclusions. So, to supplement the '00' survey, we are now collecting quadrat data for selected areas and habitats within each 1km square. A quadrat size of 2m has been chosen as we wish to compare our results with those obtained in recent Scottish surveys. In the 2m quadrats we record the area occupied by each species, note the relevant environmental factors, and collect a soil sample for detailed analysis.

One of the main problems of this type of survey in the past has been the analysis of the data. But, with the advent of computers, this task is relatively easy. Projects of this type are ideal for a team of keen amateur and professional botanists with the latter having access to computer facilities. This applies particularly to the compilation of county and regional Floras which can be made far more informative if details are provided on changes in distribution, and the reasons for these changes, in addition to supplying lists of localities in which the species have been found. This extention of the original '00' survey appears to be providing us with the type of data we require to determine the environmental tolerance of species and, furthermore, it is now revealing that there are considerable differences in tolerance within the same species depending on location and habitat.

Rather more detailed work is being carried out at the University College of Wales, Aberystwyth on certain areas which are particularly heterogeneous for both environmental factors and habitats. For this we are using association analysis and other techniques. So far, most workers have used association analysis methods for examining the vegetation in just a single area but, as Williams and Lambert (1960) have pointed out, these methods of finding associations between species and relating distribution to environmental factors are especially suitable for general survey work covering a large area. To date our work has been mainly concerned with hill-pastures and we have selected areas consisting of a mosaic of different sub-habitats and plant associations. Four areas have already been investigated but we intend to extend the survey and to resample at ten-yearly intervals.

Recording climatic change

One of the main difficulties in surveys of this type is relating changes in vegetation to changes in local climate. The information obtained by the Meteorological Office and others from Stevenson's Screens some 1·5m above ground level can be of some value, but what we need is records of day to day and seasonal changes where the more interesting species occur and, in particular, records relating to climate just above ground level and in the soil. The ideal would be to have a number of comprehensive, and preferably automatic, environmental weather stations recording in the more important nature reserves. A start has been made, but the high cost of the instruments inevitably means that we cannot obtain an overall picture of the extremes that occur which are so important to the proper understanding of plant/climate relationships.

The complex interaction of climatic and other factors can lead to changes in the distribution patterns of all species. Furthermore, climatic factors can act indirectly through modifying the soil and the distribution of species, both above and below ground level, which compete with the particular species we are investigating. Competition between species may be more important than was first realised: it is now known that certain species produce toxic substances which inhibit the germination and growth of other species.

Changes in nature reserves

Nature reserves frequently provide the most dramatic illustrations of how the distribution of species can be rapidly modified as a result of micro-climatic changes brought about by bad reserve management. In several instances a heavily grazed species-rich reserve has, within a few years, become a species poor reserve dominated by *Dactylis glomerata* and *Deschampsia cespitosa* because a fence was put around the reserve and no regular grazing allowed. By their vigorous growth, these two rank species of grass radically altered the climate, at and just above, ground level. As they grew the patches between the clumps of grass became overgrown, the amount of light reaching the ground decreased, and the soil became moister and cooler as evaporation was reduced. As a result many of the smaller and more interesting species of both plants and animals, for which the reserve was established, have become extinct. This illustrates why it is most important to find out the environmental factors which control the growth of the more interesting species which we wish to preserve: in most instances it is best to maintain the same management policy since it was the system of previous land-use that led to the area being sufficiently interesting for it to be acquired as a nature reserve in the first instance.

Perhaps we should look ahead and consider whether we should alter the micro-climate of parts of our larger reserves to create new climates which would lead to additional species coming into the reserve preferably on their own accord rather than being deliberately introduced. This would help us in our study of the effect of climate on various species since we could then see how quickly the new species arrived, how rapidly they spread, and whether they maintained themselves or gradually decreased after reaching a certain level, to be replaced by more successful, later, introductions. By doing this we shall find out just how the climate affects all the species in our reserves: this, one hopes, will result in the production of efficient management plans designed to maintain the diversity of both the environment and the species within our reserves.

REFERENCES

BRADSHAW, A. D. (1960).   Population differentiation in *Agrostis tenuis* Sibth. *New Phytol.* **59,** 92-103.

CLAUSEN, J. D., KECK, D. D. and HIESEY, W. M. (1940).   Experimental studies on the nature of species.   *Publs Carnegie Instn* **520.**

GODWIN, H. (1956).   *The History of the British Flora.*   Cambridge.

GREEN, F. H. W. (1968).   Persistent snowbeds in the western Cairngorms. *Weather* **23,** 206-209.

SPINK, P. C. (1968).   Scottish snowbeds in summer, 1967.   *Weather* **23,** 209-211.

SPINK, P. C. (1969).   Scottish snowbeds in summer, 1968.   *Weather* **24,** 115-117.

WILLIAMS, W. T. and LAMBERT, J. M. (1960).   Multivariate methods in plant ecology, II.   *J. Ecol.* **48,** 689-710.

DISCUSSION

C. J. CADBURY asked whether Dr. Savidge had found any clines in flower colour in relation to microclimate in Wales: he had found a change in *Cirsium palustre* in Monmouthshire from nearly 100% white at 1,000 ft to nearly 100% purple at 750 ft only a mile away.

DR. SAVIDGE said it had been noticed in *Silene vulgaris:* it applied not only to flower colour but to the pigmentation of the whole plant.   The physiological importance of the pigmentation is not understood.

DR. F. MERTON asked what sampling has been done to obtain adequate paramenters of the climate.

DR. SAVIDGE replied that they had sampled over 1,300 quadrats in which over 200 species had been recorded.   This gave a good range of parameters for any particlar species: however at present they had not been able to measure the microclimate directly.

M. JONES asked how the microclimate in a nature reserve might be altered.

DR. SAVIDGE said this could be achieved by the creation of small pools, by planting trees in open landscapes or by creating glades in woods.

THE RESPONSE OF PLANTS TO CLIMATE AND CLIMATIC CHANGE

C. D. Pigott

Department of Biological Sciences,
University of Lancaster

Macroclimate and plant distribution

One of the generally accepted principles of plant geography is that the distribution of plants is primarily controlled by climate (Cain 1944, p. 10-12). This principle was originally recognised in the broad correlation of different types of vegetation with the main climatic regions of the continents and is supported by the tendency for the boundaries of distribution of many individual species to follow, sometimes very precisely, the isometric lines of particular climatic variables.

Examination of the maps in the *Atlas of the British Flora* (Perring and Walters 1962) shows that a very large proportion of higher plants have their main area of distribution within the British Isles limited by a boundary which is probably related to climate, so that climatic changes would be expected *a priori* to result in changes in distribution.

Although comparative studies of the physiology of plants have shown that there are marked differences between species in their responses to variations in many of the components of climate and these must be the main cause of differences in distribution, it must be admitted that attempts to provide a really satisfactory explanation for a distribution boundary in terms of physiological responses have been generally unsuccessful. This is not entirely unexpected in view of the great complexity of the responses of plants to the no less complex variables which constitute climate. What is less easily excused is the neglect of this complexity and as a result "plant geography is rife with . . . . poorly founded conclusions as to causation." (Cain 1944, p. 17). Many recent publications show that these words written twenty-five years ago are still essentially true.

A close correlation between the distribution boundary of a species and an isometric line of a climatic variable is strong evidence that the distribution of the species is controlled by climate and it provides an indication of the particular component of climate to which the species is responding, but it does not identify the cause of the limitation. Thus, for example, the eastern boundary of *Rubia peregrina* in Western Europe is closely correlated with the January isotherm for 40°F (4·4°C) (Salisbury 1926, p. 318) but this is an average value and much lower temperatures occur each winter

in many of the plant's native localities.   Moreover, plants obtained
from Devon and grown in the north of England were found to be
undamaged in February 1969 when the ground was frozen to a
depth below 20 cm. and grass minimum temperatures of –16°C
were recorded in the immediate vicinity.

Many so-called Atlantic species have a distribution analogous
to that of *Rubia* and the eastern limit is closely correlated with an
isotherm for the coldest months.   The most thoroughly investigated
is *Ilex aquifolium* which is native in those parts of Europe which
have a mean temperature in January warmer than 0°C (Enquist
1929).   In a more detailed analysis by Iversen (1944) it is demonstrated that the presence of *Ilex* is indeed closely correlated with
the winter temperature (–0·5°C) in those parts of Denmark where
the mean temperature of the warmest month is above 16°C but,
where the summers are cooler, it is restricted to areas with a milder
winter.

This close correlation suggests that the eastern limit of *Ilex*
in Europe is a response to low temperatures in winter, but it does
not define the response.   As the boundary is approached, *Ilex*
becomes increasingly restricted to woodlands and it is possible that
photosynthesis in mild winter weather when the tree canopy is
leafless becomes of critical importance to the survival of the species;
on the other hand, *Ilex* may be susceptible to injury by frosts.
Discovery of the cause of the close correlation requires critical
analysis by observation and experiment.

Towards its eastern limit in central Europe, as for example,
in the Jura, although *Ilex* occurs in woodlands, its height does not
exceed the depth of snow.   Iversen (1944) reports severe damage
and death of *Ilex* in Denmark during the severe winters between
1939 and 1942, apparently caused by frost injury to the cambium.
The species suffered similarly in Britain during the very cold weather
of January 1963.   These winters were, of course, exceptional and
emphasise the need to take into account the variation from the mean
which can be expected.   If sensitivity to severe frost is the cause of
the eastern limit, then it suggests that there should be a simple
relation between the probability of the occurrence of injurious
temperatures and the mean monthly temperatures (reduced to sea-
level) on which the isotherm is based.   In fact, in Britain the largest
negative deviations of monthly mean temperatures occur in January
and February and may exceed 5°C.   The daily minima may be over
20°C below the mean (Bilham 1938).   Rubner (1960) believes
the boundary of *Ilex* is determined by frost injury at about –12°C.

Two other important points need emphasis.   Normally the
exposed parts of a plant are not at the same temperature as the
air and at night, especially on clear nights, they will normally be
cooler (Geiger 1961).   Secondly, leaving aside the possibility of
genetic variation in frost sensitivity, the temperature causing injury
is subject to variation, as the susceptibility of the individual depends
on conditions experienced in the period immediately preceding

exposure. Many species, though not all, if exposed to temperatures near freezing, show a physiological change known as "hardening" which involves a redistribution of water and enables the plant to withstand much lower temperatures than unhardened plants. The ability of *Ilex* to harden probably explains the severe injury or

FIGURE 1

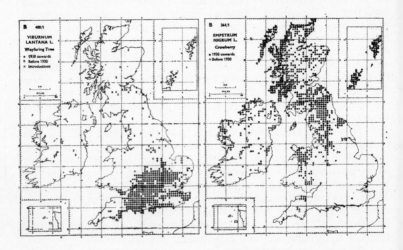

Distribution of *Viburnum lantana* and *Empetrum nigrum*.

FIGURE 2

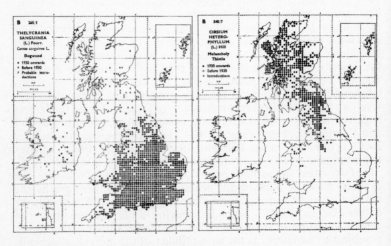

Distribution of *Thelycrania sanguinea* and *Cirsium heterophyllum*

death of the bushes during 1963 in western England and the absence
of severe damage, for example, near Cambridge where the plant
was finally exposed to much lower temperatures (–17°C on several
nights in January).

A very large number of native plants in Britain show a boundary
to their main area of distribution which runs diagonally from
south-west to north-east and is therefore at right angles to the
boundary shown by many Atlantic species. The significance of
boundaries with this orientation has been discussed by Salisbury
(1932) who concluded that they are essentially determined by climate.
There is, of course, a correlation in Britain between geological
structure and climate. The north and west of the British Isles are
formed of palaeozoic rocks and these old and often hard rocks
form extensive uplands which lie across the main pathway of the
frontal weather systems from the Atlantic. This shelters the lowlands of south-east England which are largely formed of mesozoic
and younger rocks and have a more continental climate.

There is substantial evidence of a general nature to support the
view that this type of boundary is primarily determined by climate.
In general, species which have a northern limit along this axis
occur in southern and central Europe and often show a similar
boundary either across Scandinavia (Sterner 1922; Hulten 1950) or
further south, while species which have a southern limit along this
axis show a north-western or montane distribution in Europe as a
whole. For most species the correlation with the geological
boundary is by no means exact and some show a more southerly
boundary with this trend *(Viburnum lantana* and *Empetrum nigrum)*

FIGURE 3

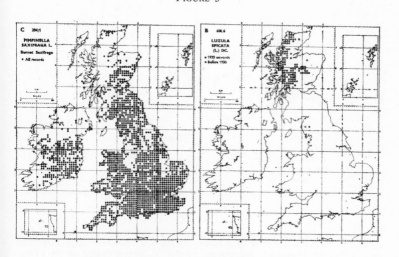

Distribution of *Pimpinella saxifraga* and *Luzula spicata*.

Fig. 1) and some a central boundary *(Thelycrania sanguinea and Cirsium heterophyllum)* (Fig. 2) and some a more northerly boundary *(Pimpinella saxifraga* and *Luzula spicata)* (Fig. 3). It is also significant that species of otherwise very different ecological requirements and therefore different distributions in detail, may show closely similar patterns of distribution. This is well illustrated by *Trollius europaeus* and *Vaccinium vitis-idaea,* or by *Myosoton*

FIGURE 4

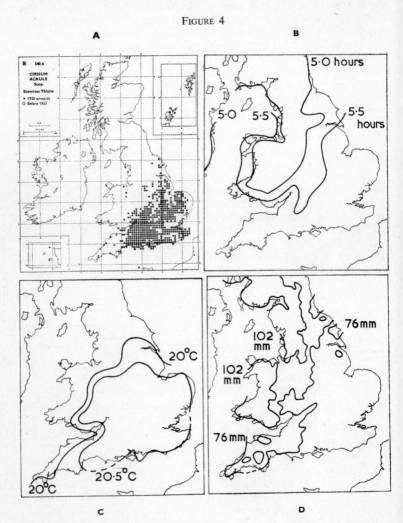

Distribution of (a) *Cirsium acaule* compared with (b) the average means of daily duration of bright sunshine in August, (c) average means of daily maximum temperature in August and (d) average rainfall in August (based on the *Climatological Atlas*).

aquaticum, *Picris hieracioides* and *Lamiastrum galeobdolon*. It is immediately apparent that boundaries with this trend in Britain and in north-west Europe generally show a correlation with particular isotherms of summer temperature, with the isometric lines for duration of bright sunshine during the summer and with the sohyets of summer rainfall (Fig. 4) (Climatological Atlas; Sjörs 1965). All these aspects of climate are of course related to the distribution of cloudiness and the interception by clouds of incoming solar radiation.

The influence of microclimate on Cirsium acaule

Such a situation gives little indication of the mechanism of climatic control and the most helpful means of analysis is to investig-ate the responses of species at the boundary, taking account of the variation between years and the influence of microclimate. Such an analysis has been attempted for *Cirsium acaule* and some of the results have recently been published (Pigott 1968). The evidence of climatic control of the distribution of this species is considerable. It shows an increasing sensitivity to aspect in its distribution as its north-western limit is approached (Fig. 5) and its reproductive capacity, including both fruit production and occurrence of estab-lished seedlings, declines (Fig. 6).

The cause of the decline in production of fruit is complicated. The initiation of flower heads is dependent on vernalization and exposure to a daily light period exceeding about 15 hours, so that

FIGURE 5

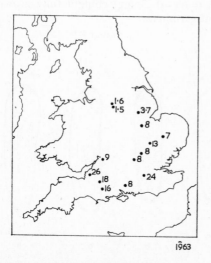

1963

Mean number of achenes with fully developed embryos per capitulum in samples collected in September 1963 at fourteen sites.

FIGURE 6

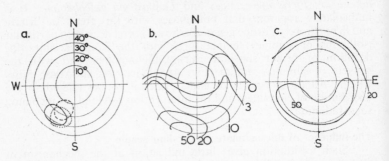

Distribution and mean number of rosettes per square metre of *Cirsium acaule* in (a) north Derbyshire (solid line, Tideswell; broken line, Wardlow Hay Cop; dotted line, Wolfscote Hill), (b) Long Dale in central Derbyshire and (c) the North Downs in Surrey in relation to slope and aspect.

flower-heads begin to develop in June. The rate of development increases with temperature so that the first flowers usually open in late June in southern, eastern and central England, but not until early August in Derbyshire. About five weeks elapse from the opening of the outer flowers in the head to the detachment of the fruit from the capitulum. At detachment the fruits may be classified in three categories (Fig. 7) which are most easily distinguished by weight. The lightest fruits (0.27 ± 0.01 mg) are shrivelled and never contain embryos. The intermediate class (1.37 ± 0.08 mg) are collapsed and often contain immature embryos, while the heaviest fruits (4.69 ± 0.13 mg) contain fully grown embryos and these alone will germinate.

FIGURE 7

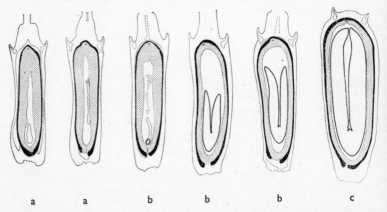

Longitudinal sections of achenes at abscission (a) unfertilized, (b) fertilized but with partly grown embryos and (c) with fully grown embryos.

The proportions of these types of fruit in any one capitulum may vary widely. This is illustrated (Fig. 8) by analyses of production of fertile fruit by plants grown in a walled, south-facing garden in Sheffield during 1960. The plants were divided by small asbestos screens so that the flower heads on the north side were shaded from the sun. The two clones differ significantly and this source of variation probably has a genetic basis. In both plants, the proportions of fertile fruits produced in each capitulum decreases as the summer passes, but there is no obvious correlation with weather during the period of development after pollination. At all times a lower proportion of fertile fruits develop in shaded flower-heads.

The proportion of shrivelled fruits depends on the proportion of flowers pollinated or ovules fertilised. In each ring of flowers, the stigma appears to remain receptive for 24–48 hours and weather certainly affects the frequency of visits by insects and may thus influence the chance of pollination. The proportion of the two heavier classes of fruits appears to depend on temperature and this can be demonstrated experimentally by altering the temperature of heads by shading them or enclosing them after pollination in transparent envelopes. The development of the embryo either directly requires high temperatures or its growth rate increases with temperature, so that the embryo is fully grown when the fruit becomes detached. Experimentally the most severe reduction in fruit production can be caused by spraying the heads with water each morning. The amount of water which lodges in the head is normally about 0·4–0·6 g so that about 240–360 calories is required to dry the head and this is a substantial proportion of the energy income during the day, so that the effect could operate through cooling or directly by reducing the rate of drying out of the developing heads. In moist conditions, heads also commonly become infected by *Botrytis cinerea* causing rotting of the head or the development of sclerotia on the fruits.

By the middle of September, the majority of fruit heads in Derbyshire are infected by *Botrytis* and few contain fertile fruits. When the late summer is cold and wet, many buds fail to open. In southern England all flowers have opened by September and even the last to develop may still produce fertile fruits and infection by *Botrytis* is largely confined to plants growing in long grass.

The overall result of the shortening of flowering period, the slow development of embryos and the spread of *Botrytis* is a reduction in production of fertile fruit by a flowering rosette from 2–300 fruits in many years in southern England to none in many years and not more than 20–50 in warm dry years in north Derbyshire.

The experiments show that temperature of the flower heads is probably critical in the development of embryos, but this will be closely dependent on incoming radiation in a plant whose flowers are in the boundary-layer of the ground surface and the heating effect of radiation will be inextricably related to the water relations

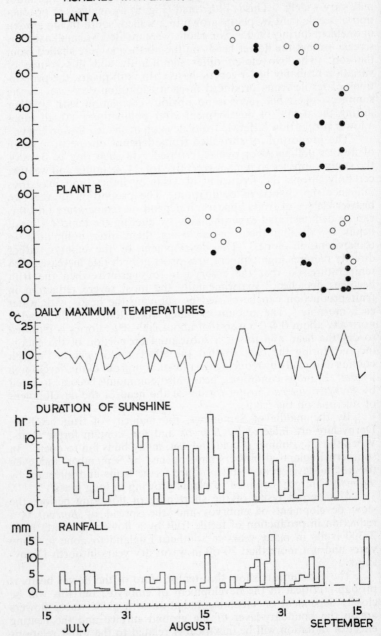

FIGURE 8

ACHENES WITH EMBRYOS PER CAPITULUM

Number of achenes with fully developed embryos per capitulum from two plants grown in Sheffield in relation to date of abscission. Each plant was divided by an asbestos screen placed east to west and capitula on the north side are shown by closed circles and those on the south by open circles. Weather records for the same period are also presented.

through the dissipation of energy in evaporation. Fruit development is clearly controlled by all the components of climate with which the distribution of the species is correlated (Fig. 8).

The ecological significance of the failure to produce fertile fruits, at least in a species whose rapid spread and dispersal cannot be achieved vegetatively, is not immediately obvious, neither is it easy to devise methods to measure the effects. Even in annual weeds, which are essentially opportunist species, there must be an excess production of seed for a species to maintain itself and it is not easy to determine what reduction in the amount of seed produced will endanger its persistence in a particular locality. It is probably significant that many annuals such as *Mercurialis annua*, *Kickxia elatine* and even *Melampyrum arvense* regularly produce fertile seed in northern England, well to the north of the limits of their main distribution area.

In long-lived perennial species, such as *Cirsium acaule*, although the problem is even more difficult to investigate, the ecological significance is not essentially different. Decreased production of fertile fruits deprives many species of the ability to establish new individuals and thus to consolidate their position in a habitat or exploit new habitats. In this way they are less able to accommodate short-term and long-term ecological changes. This effect is clearly displayed in the behaviour of *Thelycrania sanguinea* in Britain. In south-eastern England, *Thelycrania* fruits profusely and seedlings are frequent. This enables the shrub to invade abandoned arable land and pastures when grazing is relaxed and even to dominate the scrub on such sites (Lloyd and Pigott 1967). In Derbyshire and northwest England, fertile fruit is very rarely produced and *Thelycrania* spreads almost entirely by suckers. As a result it takes little or no part in the invasion of pasture by scrub and remains a relatively rare species of long-established woodland (Pigott 1969). The disappearance of a species from localities close to the limits of its distribution is to be expected if ecological change is intensified and this could occur without any change in climate, though it might well be mistaken as evidence for such a change.

Transplant experiments and artificial sowings have both been used in attempts to assesss the significance of the reduction in reproductive capacity of *Cirsium acaule* at the boundary of its distribution. Adult plants transplanted to a north-facing slope at Tideswell in Derbyshire have persisted for twelve years and spread vegetatively in the natural turf, but they flower very late, no fertile fruits have been recorded and no seedlings have become established. On the south-facing slope *C. acaule* is abundant and has clearly spread by establishment of seedlings to form a population of about 330 separate plants. Fruits have also been sown on both north and south slopes. In most dales it is very difficult to find suitable plots in north-facing slopes which will match the natural habitats because the sward is usually denser and small bare patches of soil are very sparse. In many sites the soil is also significantly more acid. At Tideswell, for example, samples of the top 1·5 cm of soil from equal numbers of sites distributed at random on the two opposite slopes of the valley gave a mean pH of 6·7 for the south slope where *Cirsium acaule* is present and 4·8 for the north slope. Less than 5% of the north slope has a pH above 6·0. These differences in the slopes arise from the differences in the amount of radiation they receive which controls the loss of water by evaporation. However, even when fruits were sown at high densities on sites selected to avoid these differences, although occasional seedlings have become established in the south-facing plots, none were successful on the north-facing plots. The fate of seedlings was not observed but damping-off commonly occurs in seedlings of *C. acaule* on moist shaded sites and could account for high mortality. At Long Dale near Elton, where *C. acaule* is abundant on the south-facing slope, occasional plants are present on the opposite slope.

FIGURE 9

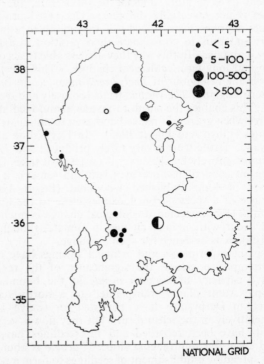

Distribution and size of populations of *Cirsium acaule* on the limestone outcrop of Derbyshire (open circle, female; closed circle; hermaphrodite half-closed, female and hermaphrodite).

These occupy a steep and unstable slope where the mineral soil is exposed and the mean pH in the top 1·5 cm of the soil is 7·4 and not significantly different from the south-facing slope with a mean pH of 7·3.

It is instructive to compare the behaviour of the species at Tideswell and Long Dale, though perhaps unwise to base too much significance on only two sites. In both sites the populations on the south-facing slopes are large (over 300 plants) and the species has probably been established well over a century. Both sites are in narrow valleys with north-facing slopes immediately opposite. Tideswell is at a higher altitude and in an area of higher rainfall and fertile fruit is produced only in exceptional years. At Long Dale fertile fruit is produced more plentifully. In this period no seedlings have become established on the north slope at Tideswell and not more than ten at Long Dale. There is evidence of successful establishment of seedlings in other localities on the Derbyshire limestone. The species is present in two other large populations in Derbyshire at Wardlow Hay Cop and Wolfscote Hill, both on south-facing slopes and there are eight other known localities, of which six consist of single plants (Fig. 9). It has been possible to age one of these single plants accurately and it was a seedling in 1948 or 49 and could have originated from fruit ripened in the warm summer of 1947, or a seedling established in the warm summer of 1949. In all but the largest population, only one of the two sexes of the species is present, which would be expected if each population had arisen from a single plant. Indeed, the whole pattern of distribution, not only in Derbyshire, but also in the Yorkshire Wolds and Welsh borderland, suggests that *Cirsium acaule* is slowly spreading, but this could have several different explanations and there is no evidence which suggests that it is in response to a change in climate.

Acknowledgements

I wish to thank the Director of the City of Sheffield Museums for permission to publish the meteorological measurements presented in Fig. 8 and Mr. E. Barron for preparing sections of developing achenes.

REFERENCES

BILHAM, E. G. (1938). *The Climate of the British Isles.* London.

CAIN, S. A. (1944). *Foundation of Plant Geography.* New York.

Climatological Atlas of the British Isles. (1952). Meteorological Office. London

ENQUIST, F. (1929). Studier över samtidiga växlingar i klimat och växlighet. *Meddn Lunds geogr. Instn* C 47.

GEIGER, R. (1961). *Das Klima der Bodennahen Luftschicht.* Braunschweig.

HULTEN, E. (1950). *Atlas över Växternas Utbredning i Norden.* Stockholm.

IVERSEN, J. (1944). *Viscum, Hedera* and *Ilex* as climate indicators. *Geol. För. Stockh. Förh.* **66**, 463-483.

LLOYD, P. S. and PIGOTT, C. D. (1967).   The influence of soil conditions on the course of succession on the chalk of southern England.   *J. Ecol.* **55,** 137-146.

PERRING, F. H. and WALTERS, S. M. (1962).   *Atlas of the British Flora.* London.

PIGOTT, C. D. (1968).   Biological Flora of the British Isles.   *Cirsium acaulon* (L). Scop.   *J. Ecol.* **56,** 597-612.

PIGOTT, C. D. (1969).   The status of *Tilia cordata* and *T. platyphyllos* on the Derbyshire limestone.   *J. Ecol.* **57,** 491-504.

RUBNER, K. (1960).   *Die Pflanzengeographischen Grundlagen des Waldbaues.* Radebeul.

SALISBURY, E. J. (1926)   The geographical distribution of plants in relation to climatic factors.   *Geogrl J.* **57,** 312-335.

SALISBURY, E. J. (1932).   The East Anglian Flora.   *Trans. Norfolk Norwich Nat. Soc.* **13,** 191-263.

SJÖRS, H. (1965).   Features of land and climate. The Plant Cover of Sweden. *Acta phytogeogr. suec.* **50,** 1-12.

STERNER, R. (1922).   The continental element in the flora of South Sweden. *Geogr. Annlr* **4.**

DISCUSSION

Mr. M. BROWN asked how important biotic factors might be in acting as agents in the climatic control of the distribution of plants: the incidence of fungal attack by *Botrytis* in high humidity areas was one example, and perhaps slug damage might be greater in high rainfall than in areas of low rainfall.

Prof. PIGOTT said that in Derbyshire as more seeds are already carrying sclerotia of *Botrytis* it means that they are carrying the seeds of their own destruction.   In experiments on the effect of shade on the growth of *Cirsium acaule* seedlings he found it necessary to surround them with a screen of slug pellets.

Dr. S. R. J. WOODELL asked whether there was any evidence of the spread of *Cirsium acaule* following the spread of myxomatosis.

Prof. PIGOTT replied that from general ecological knowledge the species would doubtfully benefit from the absence of rabbits but it had recently apparently reached some new dales in Derbyshire: he had found single plants on a number of south-facing slopes.

THE CHANGING PATTERN OF AGRICULTURE

P. J. O. TRIST

National Agricultural Advisory Service.
Bury St. Edmunds

The state of the land in 1940

At the beginning of the late war, the nation was faced with an abandoned agriculture which had been policy over the previous 15 years. In most counties and particularly in the eastern region, there were tens of thousands of acres of derelict grass, vast stretches overgrown by bushes together with derelict woodland. The attack on our merchant shipping made it imperative immediately to look to our own food supply; so the war on the land started and the derelict countryside was subsequently brought into arable production. There followed an intensive period when many of the habitats of our native flora were temporarily or permanently destroyed. The thorn bushes were removed and the land was ploughed and put into full fallow with the intention of eradicating grass and other weed flora. The hedges were cut back, not removed as we now see, the ditches were dug out and the land was subsequently underdrained. Thousands of acres were acid and poor in nutrients so lime was applied and inorganic fertiliser was used in quantities which the land had never known before. During the period of the war, comparatively little use was made of sprays as very little was known at that time of the use of chemicals on the land. Di-nitro-ortho-cresol was used on cereals, and sulphuric acid on potatoes. By the early fifties, hormone sprays were introduced and in the succeeding years more and more chemicals with specific action against individual species of weeds were developed to clean the land. At the same time plant breeders continued to produce varieties of cereals capable of heavier yields. Research work continued to show the value of an adequate and balanced use of fertilisers on both arable and grassland.

The change of countryside pattern from the early fifties

A glance at the old 6 inch Ordnance Survey maps shows how the fields were laid out in the sixteenth century and in the succeeding eras of enclosures. For the most part the boundaries indicate an elementary form of drainage by open ditches before the introduction of underdrainage which for many reasons, but mainly economic, was not general practice until the post-war years. In many cases the hedges sprung up naturally alongside the ditch, whilst in some they were planted. As can still be seen today, the small farms are comprised of very small fields, often of less than 5 acres, and therefore represented closely open-drained land as opposed to the larger fields where open ditches were further apart indicating that the land was not so wet. This interpretation of the field boundaries mainly relates to the heavy land.

Despite the sound modern criticism of the spoiling of the countryside by hedge removal on a vast scale, the old pattern had to change with the introduction of large powerful equipment such as the combine harvester and the tractor which needed a long economic run in the field. In addition modern crop yields required improved drainage systems and together with the loss of labour and its increasing cost for maintaining hedges and ditches, the increase in the size of fields was inevitable. This not only improved the facilities for a better drainage layout but coped with the loss and cost of labour which hedge maintenance demanded. In addition the farmer looked at the large trees in the hedges and in parkland which had been brought into cultivation and had to conclude that their shade and large rooting system were in conflict with the ripening of corn and the demand for moisture. All the time land was rising in value thus demanding the use of every acre. This change which has taken place has been inevitable and will continue as the costs of the farming industry rise. All of this action has in consequence had a very considerable effect in destroying or altering the great diversity of habitats for our flora which the farmland on all of the different soil types provide.

Of all of the many changes and improvements which have taken place on the land since 1940, drainage must be considered the most important. The system of mole draining if done under opportune conditions has a shattering effect on the soil which assists the movement of water to the pipes and subsequently to the ditches. A waterlogged soil has a bad effect on soil structure which impedes crop growth and inevitably is the cause of losses through late drilling.

This improvement in soil conditions has turned the *Juncus-Agrostis* areas into dry arable land where the young growth of a weed is tolerated only up to the three or four leaf stage of a cereal, after which the cereal is susceptible to damage from certain herbicides.

From the early fifties the supply and use of ditching excavators accelerated and this, coupled with the introduction of herbicides in subsequent years to kill bank and water weeds, helped to reduce maintenance costs on the farm and improve manufacturing profits but at the same time one more habitat was deducted from the botanists' list. This loss has become increasingly real in the past 10 years, for as field size has increased, the former dividing ditches have been filled, piped and covered.

In the paper which follows on herbicides, Mr. Fryer will deal with this matter in detail but some comments must be made at this point to complete my picture. The cereal producer in particular must control such weeds as *Agropyron repens*, *Agrostis gigantea*, *Alopecurus myosuroides* and the *Avena* spp. We are glad to see the last of *Allium vineale* and *Calystegia sepium* in corn crops, but in spite of herbicides, there are still big problems in the fens with *Polygonum* spp. and *Cerastium fontanum* and on the sands with *Chenopodium* spp. and *Polygonum aviculare*, and on the clays with *Sinapis arvensis* and *Galium aparine*. However, there are many farms where both good husbandry and herbicide spraying have been practised for a great number of years where weeds are now few. However it must be admitted that there are many acres unnecessarily sprayed in order to rid the land of the last small *Veronica*, *Anagallis* and *Viola*. This is in part due to pride but also to commercial sales pressure. This can cause unexpected disasters as there are herbicides on the market which are distinctly dangerous to specific crops on certain soils.

Aerial spraying becomes more popular and drift adds to the hazard over field and hedgerow. However, the increase in aerial spraying will be slow, for whilst the cost of maintenance and depreciation of the fixed wing aircraft is about £4,000 per year, it is £10,000 for the helicopter. Undoubtedly the farming community must accept some responsibility for the loss of flora from spraying and particularly from drift, but both spraying and cutting carried out by some Highway Authorities are equally irresponsible.

The present and future occupation of land

Of the national total of about 375,000 farms there are some 42,000 large farms (11%) which produce half of our total output, whilst another quarter of the output is produced by 63,000 medium-sized farms. This leaves about 269,500 small and part-time farms, many of which will inevitably be absorbed into larger units as the pressure of farm costs becomes too great for them to bear. This movement towards larger units has been going on for some years. Broadly speaking, the areas up to 100 and 150 acres are being taken over by the medium sized farms. As an example on a county basis, 430 small farms in Suffolk were taken into larger units in the two years between 1967 and 1969.

This means a decreasing number of individual farmers and the vast capital investment in agriculture will increasingly be under company control which will be forced to farm with the sole criterion of maximum profit.

The loss of farm workers is alarming. Not only do we annually lose many thousands but youth is not entering the industry for replacement. In the counties of the eastern region, there was a loss of 19,867 workers or 11 per cent between 1965 and 1968. For England and Wales over the same period, this loss was 83,146 workers, or 18 per cent.

Land values have continued to rise and although checked at the moment by the credit squeeze, will undoubtedly rise again as the demand for land to be set aside for other purposes continues. At the present time some 50-60,000 acres per year are lost to development of all kinds. There will therefore be less idle land. Not only will there be changes in ownership but there will be more intensive arable farming particularly in the east, south and parts of the south-west.   The hill and grassland areas of the west and the north will probably remain as family farms and changes in farm structure will be slower, but where capital can be found, livestock production will increase.   By the turn of the century it is estimated we shall have an increase of about 15 million people and we must guess at the increased number of car owners on the road, many of whom will be seeking relaxation in the countryside.   Employment will change to a four-day week.   There will therefore be a desperate need for education in the deployment of the increased leisure hours.

In the poorer farming areas we shall see great changes in the use of land by afforestation, picnic sites, country parks and, we hope, more sites for conservation.   Such changes are already underway.

The new attitude towards land use

I have referred to the need for education in the use of the countryside for leisure.   The farmer has a difficult time in front of him and will find that he may have to reappraise his position as an occupier and assent to the fact that his land is part of the national heritage: he must be given the opportunity to understand more about the values he has in his diversity of habitats.   He will be called upon to put up with much nuisance and at the same time will be asked to recognise the increasing appeal of country life.

The National Agricultural Advisory Service of the future will I think be tempered with an appreciation for the needs of conservation.   Our advisers will have to see that this matter is built into the pattern of the policy being advised to farmers as part of the income to be derived from a long term process.   They should give a balanced view where advice is needed on the replanning of a farm and not recommend the wholesale destruction of habitats of plant and animal life.

The Ministry of Agriculture, Fisheries and Food has always given serious consideration to applications for the reclamation of woodland before grants have been given and since the passing of the recent Countryside Act there has been even closer surveillance. The Ministry is already strict in its advice and in grant aid for areas requiring an excessive cost for drainage.   Consideration is already being given to encouraging the introduction of shelter belts and this advice can go further in general conservation particularly in the interests of farm game.   The Ministry of the future will give increasing opportunities by direct advice and conferences to assist the farmer in his appreciation for the need of conservation.   Whilst the general public will benefit, the main aim should be to improve the farmer's appreciation for his own good.   A start on this appreciation was made in July 1969 in a Farmer and Conservation Conference at Silsoe.

We must consider an expanded concept of land use and the very fact that more and more people in the Ministry are leaning towards an understanding of conservation means that agricultural policy should not be considered in isolation and that a good countryside policy should be for the general good and not entirely for the benefit of farming.

Summary of the effect of the changing pattern

1. There will be fewer farms and larger units.

2. Ownership will change. Already high land values and mortgage charges are causing sales so that the occupier can divert locked land capital into working capital for livestock expansion and new buildings. There will be more emphasis on company holdings with city investment.

3. Attitudes will change, for many future owners will be absentees with little countryside understanding. The company will be a hard business head seeking maximum profit. We shall see a ruthless deployment of every acre which can be shown to be economic. The manager, perhaps a former farmer in his own right, will direct the farming operations and not the policy.

4. The alteration of the field pattern will continue to change as economics and hard business factors become the sole consideration. Here we can hope for some alleviation where game has its possibilities for producing a high rent for the company city fellows and perhaps some conservation may emerge.

5. The areas of low ground requiring uneconomic drainage, the areas of difficult topography only fit for second-class grazing and the rocky high ground appear to be safe from the spoiler's hand.

6. Whilst it is admitted that there have been serious reductions and total losses in some species of our native flora, it is not felt that the use of chemicals should by any means bear all of the blame. The major factors include more intensive land use, improved drainage, the raising of fertility and the effects of higher yielding crops. *In short* it is the loss of habitats.

7. Therefore, in the areas of intensive farming in particular we must appeal to landowners and the generosity of the public to help to save the remaining habitats which are worthy of the local attention of the County Naturalists' Trusts and nationally by the Nature Conservancy. How right we are to think of the future of our plant life for "if you do not think about the future, you will not have one".

DISCUSSION

Prof. J. G. HAWKES asked whether any farmers might be persuaded to turn agricultural land into the equivalent of Country Parks or Nature Reserves.

Mr. TRIST said that he knew of a farmer from Kessingland in Suffolk who had developed 60 acres of his land for recreational use, including open water for ducks, a marsh, a children's playfield, a car park and refreshment room. In the first three months of opening in 1969 it had been visited by 20-30,000 people. Another farmer was, agriculturally speaking, cutting his hay far too late in order to help preserve 60,000 plants of fritillary. If botanists who knew of rare or local species on farmland would tell the owners of their importance, most of the sites could be saved.

Mr. J. E. LOUSLEY said that one of the most important changes was the loss of the horse. First because the permanent pastures they used to graze had now been ploughed up; and second because horse plough-teams could not plough all the arable in autumn leaving many weedy stubbles through the autumn and winter. Mechanisation had probably more impact on loss of weeds than herbisides.

Mr. E. D. WIGGINS asked whether it was true that sites like the Fritillary Meadow, which were designated as Sites of Special Scientific Interest, could be ploughed up by the farmer if he wished.

Mr. TRIST replied that the S.S.S.I. status was little more than a gentleman's agreement. It could only work with a sympathetic owner who was fully aware of the interest of the site. There was no obligation of a vendor to inform a purchaser of the status of the land.

Dr. K. MELLANBY said that under the Countryside Act, 1968, it was now possible for the Nature Conservancy to pay compensation to the owner of an S.S.S.I. for loss of income if he agreed not to plough up an area.

Mr. E. MILNE-REDHEAD said that though the power existed only one S.S.S.I. agreement of this kind was at present being negotiated by the Nature Conservancy.

Miss M. M. SIBTHORP asked whether the increasing weight of farm machinery was adversely affecting soil structure; and whether the loss of hedges and shelter-belts in eastern England is causing the loss of top soil in 'blows'.

Mr. TRIST said that compaction was becoming a serious problem. It was affecting soil structure and damaging top soil drainage. In wet seasons crops were affected. Much of the Fens of East Anglia had never had hedges, and to provide sufficient shelter-belts to prevent 'blows' would be uneconomic.

Mr. E. F. GREENWOOD asked whether there was likely to be an increase in changing pastures into caravan parks.

Mr. TRIST thought that this would grow, especially in the west, where cream teas, bed and breakfast and caravan sites were more economical than keeping 1 ewe to 5 acres.

THE EFFECT OF PLANTING TREES

M. Brown

Forestry Commission, Alice Holt,
near Farnham, Hampshire

Tree planting in Britain

In Britain there is a long tradition of planting trees, both of native species and of trees brought from overseas to supplement the relatively few species which moved in before these islands became isolated after the Quaternary glaciations. Sometimes these plantations were designed for ornament; in the 18th and 19th centuries formal groves and avenues, often of beech, were considered an essential part of any well laid out estate. Often, however, they were created, in part at least, for profit. Through the centuries there has been much planting of the common oak, *Quercus robur,* at one period largely to provide acorns for feeding pigs in winter.

Times and customs change and the prospect of producing timber more quickly, especially on hill land where oak grows slowly, encouraged many landowners to experiment with some European conifers, in addition to the native Scots pine. Larch, known in Britain as long ago as 1629, was planted more extensively on the Atholl Estates near Dunkeld from about 1730: the Norway spruce, *Picea abies*, has a rather longer history here. In the nineteenth and early twentieth centuries mixed plantations of larch, spruce and Scots pine, sometimes replacing broadleaf woods that had been cut down, more often perhaps on bare land, were often favoured. Other European trees long established in Britain are the silver fir, *Abies alba*, now seldom planted ; the sycamore, *Acer pseudoplatanus*; and the sweet chestnut, *Castanea sativa*, said to have been introduced by the Romans and well acclimatised in south and east England, where it was much grown as coppice to provide hop poles and fencing material.

Interest in some of the many coniferous timber trees of N. America may be said to date from the travels of the Scottish botanist, David Douglas, who in 1827 sent seed to Britain of the fir named after him, *Pseudotsuga menziesii*. Fast growth on sites which suit it, combined with valuable timber and an attractive appearance, ensured a firm place for the Douglas fir in reafforestation programmes. But it is not a sound choice on peat, on greatly impoverished mineral soils, or in positions much exposed to the wind. For these reasons extensive use is now made, in the afforestation of mountainous country, or of blanket peat in Scotland, of two other N. American trees, the Sitka spruce, *Picea sitchensis*, and the lodgepole pine, *Pinus contorta*. Several species of *Abies,*

Tsuga heterophylla, western hemlock and *Thuja plicata,* western red cedar are included among the other N. American conifers planted in Britain: among broadleaf trees may be mentioned the acacia, *Robinia pseudoacacia* and the red oak, *Quercus borealis.* Other lands have contributed the Chilean beeches, *Nothofagus* spp.; the Japanese larch, *Larix kaempferi*; the Corsican pine, *Pinus nigra*; and the Norway maple, *Acer platanoides.*

Aspects of current forest practice

This paper deals with the recent accelerated creation of mainly commercial plantations, mostly in the uplands of the north and west of Britain and often with some of the exotic trees referred to. Such plantations not only change the landscape in themselves, introducing new species to a locality, or altering the distribution of existing species: they may, and commonly do, affect profoundly the associated flora of shrubs, herbs and cryptogamic plants. Where mature trees already occupy the land the conditions are different and it is sometimes possible to obtain natural seeding of the native oak, ash, birch, beech, or Scots pine; or of the Douglas fir, spruce or hemlock. Very often, however, the forester wishes to use a different species for replanting; while, if he chooses the same species, he may prefer to control the race, or provenance, and the spacing, rather than try his luck with natural regeneration.

In the main, reafforestation in the last few decades, whether by private owners and co-operative groups, or by the Forestry Commission, has been on wasteland or poor mountain pasture, which is quite unsuited to grow corn or potatoes, orchards, or good grass. The conditions limit the number of species which can be used and call for more or less thorough ground preparation, if those tolerant species are to survive and grow well. The measures used to prepare the land all influence in some degree the native plant association of heath, bog or mire and merit brief notice.

1. *Drainage.* None of the trees which are widely grown will do well if the roots are subject to prolonged seasonal waterlogging. Blanket bog, wet heath and other swampy ground must, therefore, be methodically relieved of excess water; this is normally done before planting, but additional drains may be dug later if required.

2. *Cultivation.* Forest ploughs have been designed to deal with almost every kind of difficult site; whether deep peat, or rocky ridge crest, or compacted iron pan. Improved aeration and the temporary removal of competition from the native plants are among the benefits to the small planted trees.

3. *Vegetation control by other means.* On sites where ploughing is unnecessary, or impracticable (e.g. on steep slopes), or has proved insufficient, vegetation is often controlled by hand tools, machines, or chemicals.

4. *Fertilisation.* On all organic soils and most wet heaths, or dry heath podzols, application of phosphatic manure is an essential means of ensuring good early growth. Exceptionally, nitrogen and potash are also given.

5. *Fencing.* Animals such as rabbits and hares, sheep, cattle, or deer, which would bite through, or browse, the young trees, must be kept out for at least ten years.

6. *Roads.* Sooner or later (usually not until the time for removal of produce in thinnings) an effective system of forest roads will be needed.

These works all have a quick direct or indirect impact on the indigenous plant community: but they are designed to promote survival and growth of the planted trees and, insofar as they succeed, their more or less transient effect on ground plants becomes largely effaced by the influence of the trees themselves. Nevertheless, although within the stand the shade of the trees may dominate the environment, those ancillary operations will influence the responses of plants to the shade. The influence of drainage, fertilisation, fencing and pan rupture may be important and persist for a long time.

The forest environment

The first point to note is that the effect of the trees is specific: it might be better to head this section "Forest environments", so as to stress that, while all woods modify the environment in certain general directions, the habit of growth of the dominant tree or trees gives to the habitats within the wood a particular stamp. The properties mainly affected are:

1. The quantity of solar radiation available for photosynthesis.
2. Other climatic effects: reduction of wind speed and of the temperature and humidity ranges.
3. Soil water: there is greater desiccation of the soil (as a rule), due to larger interception of rain and increased transpiration through the trees.
4. Conditions in the humus layer; the surface soil and nutrient turn-over are modified.

As to 3 it is probably true to say that interspecific differences in themselves have less influence on amounts of transpired water than have differences in age and density of the stand, soil conditions for root growth, etc. Evergreen trees will, however, dispose of more rainwater by direct evaporation, because they retain a full canopy in winter. Generally broadleaf trees promote better litter breakdown and nutrient release than conifers, especially the pines and spruces, but there are important specific differences within each group.

Insofar as the ground plants and their survival, growth and propagation are concerned, much the most significant differences between trees are in the quantity of light they transmit at equivalent stages of growth. Differences in several other properties of the woodland habitat run more or less parallel with differences in canopy density and so it will be useful to give these prominence.

Among the deciduous broadleaf trees we may distinguish:

1. Those with very sparse canopies: birches, ash, also oak on base poor soil, where there are no shrubs.
2. Intermediate: oak on base rich soil, with variable shrub layer of hazel, field maple, blackthorn, etc.
3. Those with rather dense canopy: beech, elm.

Among the conifers we distinguish:

1. The deciduous larches, transmitting much radiation also in summer.
2. Evergreens with rather sparse canopies: most of the pines.
3. Evergreens with more or less dense canopies: spruces, silver firs, western hemlock.

It must however be emphasised that, within each class, the stage of growth and the thinning treatment greatly modify the light transmission: a dense young thicket of ash or oak may intercept more light in summer than a 60 years old wood of Douglas fir, several times thinned. Moreover, the general cloud amount of the locality and the aspect and slope (whether sunny or shady) are relevant, not only to light transmission, but to other properties of stand climate and surface soil.

The choice of tree

What has been written about forest environments above makes it clear that the species of tree actually used on a planting site will largely determine which species among the plants available can find suitable habitats. It is proper, therefore, to consider briefly what guides foresters in this choice among the many species, native and exotic, which have shown themselves suited by our climate, at least in some regions. In past times local experience, backed by intelligent appraisal of the heath, bog, or woodland plant communities, was the master guide: the mistakes that were made arose usually from a lack of knowledge of the climatic tolerance of some introduced tree. Ecological guidance of this sort is no less valid today, but the answers it gives are weighed by the economist, concerned mainly with production, prices and markets for the timber.

It has come about then that foresters in Britain have planted large areas of wasteland, together with small areas of former broadleaf woodland, with some highly productive evergreen conifers. On the wasteland this change is without doubt also a measure of site improvement, albeit inimical to certain of the wasteland plants (e.g. the sundews, bog asphodel and bog moss of valley mire and wet heath). It is generally true, however, that these losses are more than balanced by the creation of many new habitats for plants, at wood margins, on road verges and along the undisturbed rides, as well as within the stand. The net result is an interesting diversification of flora. On the woodland sites, besides some more problematic long term effects on the soil, there are usually immediate effects on the vegetation, although a few of the indigenous plants (e.g. the bluebell) appear very persistent. They are due in part to changes wrought, either by the trees themselves, or by silviculture, to the surface soil; in part to the cooler more equable climate under the evergreens; in the main to the shade.

It was intended that this Conference of the Botanical Society should review developments during the last 50 years. It is in fact just 50 years since the Forestry Commission began work and it will not be out of place to quote some figures for the proportions of species planted by the Commission, though it must be stressed that the area planted each year by private enterprise is also large.

Of the 1¾ million acres (700,000 hectares) of plantations held by the Forestry Commission, spruces account for 48%, pines 33%, larches 11·5% and broadleaf trees 6·5%: the two most abundant trees are Sitka spruce, 36%, and Scots pine, 18·5%. In 1967, the last year for which figures are to hand, Sitka spruce àccounted for 48% of the 21,000 hectares planted and lodgepole pine for 18·5%: but the lodgepole pine nearly all went to Scotland, where two thirds of the planting programme was carried out. In England Sitka spruce accounted for only 20% and lodgepole pine for 7% of the trees planted. Over the last ten years planting by the Forestry Commission has been at the rate of 52,000-64,000 acres (20,000-25,000 ha) a year.

Changing patterns

This Conference is about the flora of a changing Britain and it is fitting that the dynamic aspect of forest vegetation should receive mention. Certain changes take place in all plant communities, in response to climatic oscillations, grazing, disease, fire, cultivation, or other disturbance by man. In few communities is this phenomenon of movement as marked as in forests. We begin with the puny little trees, doubtfully capable of holding their own in a blanket bog, or Callunetum, a grass sward, or the bracken of a cut-over pinewood. For some years there may be a rich and varied flora of heath or forest plants, until, within the 4 m tall spruce or pine thicket, the light is virtually shut out. In a few years, however, this sombre aspect is relieved by the varying height of the trees and the effect of the woodman's axe: more light enters the wood and plants soon follow. These may be the common plants of acid woodland soil: *Dryopteris dilatata, Pteridium aquilinum, Digitalis purpurea, Hypnum cupressiforme, Hylocomium* spp; with (on mull sites) *Oxalis acetosella, Rubus fruticosus, Deschampsia caespitosa*; or (on mor) *Vaccinium myrtillus, Deschampsia flexuosa*. Changes in the humus layers due to the trees make colonisation by some species relatively easy, by others difficult or impossible. But the restrictions are doubtless due largely to lack of seeds and spores: there is still much to be learnt about the factors which control the composition of plant communities in woods after the dark phase has passed.

Questions of seed dormancy, the activities of birds and mammals, the direction and strength of the winds and the occurrence of gaps due to death or removal of trees are all relevant: in our climate, the strong winds, of which the unhappy results are at times evident to foresters, may partly explain why woods seldom keep a bare floor for long after the light becomes adequate for survival of seedlings.

As the trees become taller and more widely spaced (as a result of thinning), such plants can extend their range and gain recruits: moreover the release of plant foods around fresh stumps fosters some more exacting species, notably the willow-herb, *Epilobium angustifolium*. After the wood is eventually cut down, this plant and the foxglove may break out in a blaze of colour.

In every forest, accordingly, besides the seasonal changes affecting trees and ground plants alike, there is a longer cycle of change, coincident in managed woodland with what foresters call a rotation—the period, sometimes 50 years or less, sometimes 100 years, from seeding or planting to the harvesting of the timber. In a forest managed for sustained yield, all phases are present and so the opportunity of continued existence is offered to all plants suited by the local climate and soil, without regard to their tolerance of shade.

Conclusion

In recent decades the expansion of forests and the intensification of forest management have introduced several new trees to the British flora and extended the range of some well established exotic trees. The reduction of the native oak forests, begun in the Bronze Age and intensified with the processing of iron ore and the pasturing of sheep in medieval times, has not been arrested, in spite of the creation of new plantations of oak in many counties. Its seral associate on base rich soils, the ash, has suffered in some degree with the oak, as have field maple, hazel and wild cherry.

Adaptable species with abundant, widely scattered seeds, like the birches and sallows, and the rowan spread by birds, are in no danger from the extensive planting of conifers; while the beech will always be treasured for its beauty, even if few landowners can face the cost of creating large woods of beech, as was done in the 18th and 19th centuries.

With a slow general impoverishment in forests of deciduous broadleaf trees, there has been a loss of ground by most of our common woodland plants: the bluebell, anemone, primrose, woodruff, violet, enchanter's nightshade, dog's mercury, wood spurge, yellow archangel, bugle, sanicle, wood avens, ground ivy, lords-and-ladies, wood sedge, wood melick and male-fern—to recall some of the most familiar. Happily, none of these is in any danger of extinction, but the need is great for preservation of small oak or mixed woods in regions of Britain where these plants occur naturally.

Almost equally noteworthy is the loss of ground by many wasteland communities where the restoration of forest has been undertaken. All the widespread and abundant associations of grass-heath, dwarf-shrub heath, soligenous peat, or mire (in the terminology of McVean and Ratcliffe 1962 and Ratcliffe 1964). and ombrogenous peat, or blanket bog, have been drawn on in recent afforestation schemes. Some account of the work of the Forestry Commission in Scotland and northern England, with a description of how the considerable technical obstacles have been surmounted, is given by Zehetmayr (1954, 1960). While afforestation radically changes the composition of the plant cover, the area affected is relatively small and the enterprise has had the result of diversifying the pattern of vegetation in the Highlands, up to an altitude of 500 m, without encroaching seriously on the habitats of the plants of heath, bog and mire. Above about 500 m, exposure to wind greatly restricts afforestation.

> One impulse from a vernal wood
> May teach you more of man,
> Of moral evil and of good,
> Than all the sages can.

Surely Wordsworth had in mind an oak, or oak-ashwood, with its bright carpet of flowers under the tender green of young leaves. We may not agree with all he writes, but we will keep the vernal wood for the enjoyment of all and the inspiration of many.

REFERENCES

McVean, D. N. and Ratcliffe, D. A. (1962) *Plant Communities of the Scottish Highlands*. Monographs of the Nature Conservancy No. 1. H.M.S.O., London.

Ratcliffe, D. A. (1964). in *The Vegetation of Scotland* (ed. J. H. Burnett) Oliver & Boyd, Edinburgh & London.

Zehetmayr, J. W. L. (1954). *Experiments in Tree Planting on Peat*. Forestry Commission Bulletin No. 22. H.M.S.O., London.

Zehetmayr, J. W. L. (1960). *Afforestation of Upland Heaths*. Forestry Commission Bulletin No. 32. H.M.S.O., London.

DISCUSSION

Mr. A. P. Dunball asked whether the Forestry Commission carries out aerial spraying with 2, 4, 5-T and similar chemicals.

Mr. Brown replied that very little spraying from the air now took place, but herbicides are used from knap-sack sprayers.

Miss M. McCallum Webster said that forestry in Moray had led to over-drainage. Run-off after storms was so rapid that it had brought about changes to the rivers Findhorn and Nairn detrimental to native plants.

THE BOTANICAL IMPORTANCE OF OUR HEDGEROWS

M. D. HOOPER

Nature Conservancy,

Monks Wood Experimental Station, Huntingdon

Loss of hedges

This paper is an attempt to predict what will happen to our flora as a result of the reduction in hedgerow mileage which is taking place at the present time.

This reduction in hedgerows is quite remarkable. In the last twenty years we have lost somewhere between 4,000 and 7,000 miles of hedgerow or between 3,000 and 5,000 acres of habitat *each year!* The rate has shown no decline in recent years and hence a possible prediction is that the last hedge in England will be destroyed sometime in the first quarter of the next century.

Unfortunately the situation is not quite as simple as it first appears. We did have something just over 600,000 miles of hedge after the last war; we have been losing and are apparently continuing to lose them at a rate of the order of 6,000 miles each year, and so the last hedge should go somewhere between 2030 and 2070. But the dangers of extrapolation from the present trends are very great. There are various reasons for this. First of all we must understand why the hedges are being removed. There are three basic reasons, the cost of maintenance, the efficiency of machinery and the introduction of entirely arable farms. On entirely arable farms all hedges may go because they are *entirely* unnecessary. On mixed farms with some arable the use of larger, or rather faster, machines makes increased row lengths necessary for efficiency, and some hedges will go as fields are enlarged. The major reason for hedge removal, however, is cost. A hedge is expensive to plant and expensive to maintain. Even on a boundary line where a fence of some sort is necessary, barbed wire may well be cheaper than a hedge. However, if the hedge is straight and has been well treated in the past, then to continue to maintain it will be less costly in the long run than to grub it out and erect a wire fence.

Hence, instead of suggesting all hedges will go, it is more reasonable to suggest that the hedge mileage will be reduced to extinction in eastern England but that the reduction will be progressively less as one travels westwards. This prediction is borne out by the present rates of hedgerow removal in various parts of

the country. In arable eastern England I have found rates of up
to 10 times greater than the national average; on midland mixed
farms the rate is about half the national average and on one grass
farm in the west I have found a small but significant increase in
hedge mileage.

Loss of species

This localization of hedge destruction in the east has its bright
side. If one looks at the list of the 300 rarest species one finds about
10 species which are hedgerow plants. But most of these 10, like
Scrophularia scorodonia and *Lithospermum purpurocaeruleum*, are
western in their distribution and are probably not in immediate
danger from the destruction of their habitat. There is in fact only
one species, *Lonicera xylosteum*, which may be in immediate danger,
though I would also worry about *Cynoglossum germanicum* and
Stachys germanica.

On the national scale therefore it appears that perhaps only
three rare species may become extinct because of hedge removal.
On a local scale, however, perhaps up to about 50 species may
become extinct in individual areas such as grid squares, vice-
counties or counties in the next thirty years.

About 500 species have been recorded as occurring in hedges
at some time or another but only half these can be regarded as
hedgerow plants. For most of these species alternative habitats are
available so the problem of whether any individual species will
become extinct in, say, a county will depend upon the relative
numbers of plants of that species present in hedges as against the
alternative habitats and the relative rate of destruction of hedges as
against that of the alternative habitats.

The basic alternative habitats for hedgerow plants are the
margins of deciduous woodland, coppice, scrub and rough grassland.
All these are under pressure. Direct estimates of the rate of decline
of these are not readily available except for rough grassland, which
between 1945 and 1965 was declining over England and Wales as a
whole at a rate of 1 per cent per annum and up to twice that rate
in eastern England. For woodlands, coppice and scrub, estimates
indicate a fairly static situation with some increase in scrub on
former chalk downland. Elsewhere scrub which developed in the
1930s has been eradicated and the overall position with regard to
total acreage is relatively unchanged. There is, however, a change
in the character of the woodland. The Forestry Commission in
recent years has been replanting up to 13,000 acres in England, of
which 12,000 acres are conifer and 1,000 acres are broadleaf
plantations. If this pattern were followed by all woodland owners
the present 64% of broadleaved woodland would be down to 8%
in 50 years, so again a decline of about 1 per cent per annum might
be predicted. The hedgerow decline is also of this order so all
habitats seem to be declining at much the same rate, hence the
crucial factor for a plant is its frequency of occurrence in the various
habitats.

There are four basic situations for a hedgerow plant:

1. It may be very common and have a high proportion of its population in hedges, e.g. *Crataegus monogyna*;
2. It may be very common and have a low proportion of its population in hedges, e.g. *Vicia sativa*;
3. It may be uncommon and have a high proportion of its population in hedges, e.g. *Rosa villosa*;
4. It may be uncommon and have a low proportion of its population in hedges, e.g. *Stellaria neglecta*.

A numerical example may make this clearer.

Let us suppose there exists an area with, say, 500 plants of *Crataegus monogyna*: 330 of these, or 66%, are in hedges, 166 are in scrub, then scrub clearance at 1% per annum will eliminate 1·6 plants per annum and hedge destruction 3·3 plants per annum.

Or in the case of a rarer plant with only 50 plants in the imaginary area, of which only 10 are in hedges—hedgerow destruction will destroy only one plant every ten years.

This of course assumes random distribution of individuals which is uncommon: it is much more likely is that all ten plants of the rare species will be together in one single stretch of hedge and will be destroyed when that stretch of hedge is destroyed. But the same goes for scrub, hence the thesis that destruction will take place in proportion to the populations in the various habitats has an overall validity.

What then are the species with a high proportion of their populations in hedges and how many are there?

It is possible that 50 species will become extinct in individual localities largely as a result of hedgerow destruction in the next thirty years—this is in fact about the number of species which have a high proportion of their population in hedges, but one should not equate the two too precisely. I cannot imagine *Crataegus monogyna* becoming extinct even though most of its population exists in hedgerows but I can imagine *Sambucus ebulus* becoming extinct, although it has a lower, but still significant, proportion of its population in hedgerows.

The significant question is whether or not the loss of 50 species is important botanically. 50 species is only about 3% of our total flora and we cannot suppose that ours has ever been a static flora. Some change must be accepted and 3% spread over perhaps thirty years is a very small change, particularly when one remembers that these are local extinctions only. The plants will probably survive in some neighbouring area.

On the other hand many of these species are common ordinary plants: they make up much more than 3% of the flora of, say, a agricultural 10 km grid square in the lowlands of England. Here the percentage might well be nearer 30 than 3.

One must also remember what these hedgerow plants are— mainly Rosaceous shrubs and climbers and Umbellifers. These are among the most frequent primary producers in that most rich part of the characteristically English habitat of deciduous woodland, the woodland edge. A hedge is a woodland edge both in structure and species composition. It supports a very large number of our birds and insects. Several thousand miles of hedge may be unimportant botanically but of the greatest importance biologically.

I think the following 30 species (excluding *Rosa* and *Rubus*) may become extinct in some areas in the next 30 years largely as a result of hedgerow removal:

Shrubs

Thelycrania sanguinea   Rhamnus catharticus
Euonymus europaeus   Sorbus torminalis
Malus sylvestris   Viburnum lantana
Pyrus communis

Climbers

Bryonia dioica   Lonicera periclymenum
Clematis vitalba   Tamus communis
Humulus lupulus

To these must be added various species of *Rosa* and *Rubus* (perhaps 20 species in all depending somewhat on the classification used), especially in the aggregates *Rosa villosa* and *R. rubiginosa*.

Herbs

Umbellifers— although often thought of as roadside verge plants, many appear to need a hedge or bank: this is possibly a temperature effect.

Anthriscus caucalis   Sison amomum
Chaerophyllum temulentum   Torilis japonica
Petroselinum segetum

Others

Adoxa moschatellina   Poa nemoralis
Agrimonia odorata   Rubia peregrina
Bromus ramosus   Solidago virgaurea
Cruciata laevipes   Viola odorata
Dipsacus pilosus   Vinca major
Galium mollugo   V. minor
G. verum

DISCUSSION

Mr C. J. CADBURY reported that *Stachys germanica* had re-appeared in Oxfordshire after a hedge had been removed. Seeds perhaps remained dormant for a very long time: it was apparently adapted to exploiting glades natural or artificial.

Dr. HOOPER commented that, whilst the plant might make a temporary show following disturbance, it was another question whether it would survive long after the complete removal of the hedge.

Prof. J. G. HAWKES asked how far the hedgerow was the only habitat of a species locally, for many species there would surely be alternative sites in woods.

Dr HOOPER agreed that very few species occurred exclusively in hedges, but the alternative woodland habitat was also disappearing rapidly: the Forestry Commisssion was planting 10 acres of conifers for one acre of hardwoods.

Mr M. BROWN agreed that deciduous woodland would continue to decline in acreage in this country : it was very important that conservation organisations should acquire examples in all parts of the country so that future generations would be able to enjoy the sight of a bluebell wood in the spring.

Mr C. J. JEFFEREY asked whether it was possible to assess the total value of hedges to the community, adding together their biological and amenity value.

Dr HOOPER said this was not possible: he could say that the cost to the farmer of hedge maintenance and loss of cropping was 30/-d. to £2 per acre of his farm per annum.

Miss M. ANGUS asked whether too much blame for destroying hedges and verges was being placed on farmers: great differences could be observed between adjacent counties because of variation in the attitude of local authorities.

Dr HOOPER replied that whilst this was true of verge maintenance, it could not be true of hedge management which is the responsibility of the farmer.

Mr E. D. WIGGINS asked whether the importance of planting hedgerows as wind-breaks was widely enough known.

Dr HOOPER said that whilst the value of hedges in preventing soil erosion was appreciated in some areas, the only hedge-planting in this connection he knew of was taking place at Methwold in the Fens. These hedges were of willow, and the only ground flora was nettle. Thus they were not of great botanical interest.

Mr D. DANIELS asked whether loss of hedges would cause a reduction in the bird population which would result in a loss of dispersal agents for hedgerow shrubs.

Dr HOOPER replied that losses of birds were not as great as loss of hedges: loss of 90% of the hedges in an area probably reduced the bird population by only 30%. The birds tended to nest more closely together in the remaining hedges.

THE COLONISATION OF ESTUARIES
FOLLOWING BARRAGE BUILDING

A. J. GRAY

*Nature Conservancy, Coastal Ecology Research Station, Norwich**

Introduction

The idea that fresh water might be stored by damming estuaries at or near their mouths is not a new one; it must seem a particularly logical method to those whose job it is to conserve this increasingly precious resource, moreover it is one which is more and more likely to become a reality. At the present time Desk Studies have been published on barrage proposals for the Dee estuary, Morecambe Bay and the Solway Firth (Anon 1966a, 1966b and 1966c), proposals concerning the Wash are shortly to be considered, whilst the proposed barrage across Morecambe Bay is currently the subject of a full-scale Feasibility Study.

Were such schemes to reach fruition their impact on the environment would be both fundamental and far-reaching. For example, in one of the schemes for Morecambe Bay alone, a complex estuarine system, comprising some 30,000 acres of intertidal sand and mud-flat and 3,750 acres of salt and brackish water marsh, would be converted into a large freshwater lake containing in excess of 60,000 million gallons with a possible 15,000 acres of variously drained marginal land. The barraging of the Wash could involve an area of nearly 400 square miles (White in Lowe-McConnell 1966).

The biological consequences of changes on this scale are made difficult to foresee in detail by the shortage of precedents. A majority of the Dutch schemes has been concerned with reclamation of land for agriculture rather than with water conservation (although parts of the Ijsselmeer, and the newly enclosed Lauwers Zee may be relevant). The exclusion of the sea from the estuary of the R. Quoile by the erection of sluices in 1958 at a point where it enters Strangford Lough, north of Downpatrick in Northern Ireland, has provided an interesting example of the effect of barraging. Visits to this area and to a number of sites in Holland have emphasised that each case should be treated on its merits, and that the local

---

* Present address: Nature Conservancy, Merlewood Research Station, Grange-over-Sands.

species populations may react in a specific way to changes in local conditions. However, it ought to be possible to make certain tentative general predictions. Biologists are increasingly being asked to provide engineers and planners with practical advice, and to fail to attempt to at least frame the relevent questions, is to cast a very poor light on the achievements of ecological research over the past few decades. (The ultimate test of our notions of ecological cause and effect is their applicability to novel situations). Gilson (1966) has outlined a number of the general biological implications of barrages in Morecambe Bay and the Solway Firth. What follows here is a collection of 'first thoughts' on one aspect of the possible botanical consequences, the initial invasive stages. Based on preliminary studies in Morecambe Bay, they present a higher ratio of cerebral to experimental activity than one normally likes to come across: perhaps the final phrase of the declared aims of our conference can be offered as an apologia for introducing them here.

New habitats for old

Barrage construction will create *de novo* a variety of habitats available for colonisation by plants. They will form two groups:

1. Those within areas impounded by the barrage, including the reservoir, its margins and any enclosed 'polder' land.

2. Those on new marshes which may develop seaward of the barrage.

1. The first group of habitats may include former intertidal mud-flats which become submerged to various (and varying) depths by fresh water, former mud-flats which become temporarily or even permanently exposed within a freshwater environment, former saltmarshes in various stages of development which become submerged, and former saltmarshes which remain exposed. The extent to which such areas are created will largely be determined by the constraints imposed by engineers and hydrologists, which include the most suitable (economical) barrage line, and the most suitable top water level for the reservoir. Nevertheless, the generally flat shape of most estuaries means that the reservoirs will have extensive, shallow margins, and preliminary studies have indicated that, where it is of low agricultural value, marginal land may not be intensively used but be valued for its amenity, recreational or wildlife potential, and, providing water quality is not affected, possibly left to its own devices.

2. Retaining walls in estuaries tend to produce areas of accretion at their seaward edge. This is a well-studied physio-graphical response (Kestner and Inglis 1956, Inglis and Kestner 1958, Kestner 1961). The rate of accretion of fine sediments is increased due mainly to the reduction of the total tidal volume of the estuary and to the reduction of the velocity of the ebb flow.

(The deposition of fine silt particles from suspension is increasingly encouraged by lower ebb velocities). The resulting accretion may, as in earlier reclamation schemes in the Wash (Kestner 1962), eventually lead to the formation of new areas of saltmarsh.

The response of the local populations

In assessing the likely vegetational changes following such a dramatic reconstruction of the estuarine environment we must assume at least two things. The first is that, following the initial invasive stages, the occupation of the newly created niches by individual species will accord well with their known ecological tolerances in established semi-natural habitats: i.e. factors such as water table and nutrient status will operate in the normal limiting way. Second, we must also assume that, where they are available as local seed parents, certain species will take the maximum opportunity afforded them by the provision of new sites for colonisation. The reproductive capacity of plants in similar habitats nearby must be assumed to be at least equal to saturating any suitable new habitats with potential individuals. The dangers inherent in these assumptions are discussed later. For the present it is proposed that, in the spirit of some earlier papers, the problem of prediction should be considered.

Behind the barrage one would expect the obligate halophytes to gradually disappear. However certain species such as *Aster tripolium*, *Spergularia marina*, *Juncus maritimus* and *Armeria maritima* may gain temporary footholds in the disturbed environments, whilst *Scirpus maritimus* and *S. tabernaemontani* may remain as important members of the wetland communities. The management of the marginal land is of critical importance; in the Ijsselmeerpolders halophytes such as *Plantago maritima*, *Glaux maritima* and *Juncus gerardii* have persisted for more than 30 years in extensively grazed swards (Beeftink, personal communication).

One would expect the vegetation of the reservoir margins to be assorted according to the depth and turbidity of the water, the nutrient status of the water and the lake bed, the extent of wave disturbance, and the amount of fluctuation in water level caused by the drawing down of the reservoir. Bottom-rooted species with some tolerance of a varying water level include *Phragmites communis*, *Scirpus lacustris*, *S. tabernaemontani*, *Typha* spp. and *Eleocharis* spp. The initial high salinities may allow *Scirpus maritimus* to become an important, and possibly dominant, member of the reedswamps which could develop in water up to about 3 feet deep. *S. maritimus* persists long after saline influence is removed and has become a troublesome weed in some Dutch polders (Bakker *et al.* 1960). The development and species composition of this marginal community will vary with the factors listed above. In the Quoile Pondage area a tall reedswamp dominated by *Scirpus lacustris* and *Typha latifolia* has developed on the rich marine muds of the former beach line. By contrast less favourable conditions will exist in

Morecambe Bay where the present intertidal zones are predominantly sandy and poor in nutrients, and where wave disturbance and drawdown are likely to be greater.

The drawing down of the water level during periods of drought is likely to be a key factor in the colonisation of the shallow margins of estuarine reservoirs. Harris and Marshall (1963) have studied the effects of drawdown on emergent vegetation in waterfowl and muskrat marshes in N. America where it is used as a deliberate management technique. They conclude that the composition of the stands which develop on drawdown areas is determined by the time of drawdown, availability of seed, and soil type. They also found that, as in Holland, certain species spread dramatically in the period immediately following the exposure of bare mud-flats. In particular *Senecio palustris*, previously unknown in one area, became a major component of the vegetation, producing enough seed to colonise all available mud-flats within a few years. This species, together with *Aster tripolium*, also formed large dense stands in some Dutch polders during the second year of exposure (Bakker 1960a).

There is apparently no sure way of knowing which species may be important in colonising the bare areas created by barrage construction and subsequent drawdown. The lesson to be learned from the Netherlands is that the most unexpected may turn up. Studies on British populations of *Aster tripolium* (Gray, unpublished) show that these contain a proportion of rapidly growing, first year flowering, annual forms, which could produce sufficient numbers of wind-dispersed fruits rapidly enough to exploit new areas. Other estuarine species, at present with a limited ecological range e.g. *Atriplex*, may prove to be opportunists.

The primary invasion of the newly exposed areas and the initially open communities is most likely to be by a number of aggressive, weedy taxa, especially those which are wind disseminated. The nutrient status of the soils and the extent to which they are drained and the salt leached from them will largely determine which species are successful. In the drier areas and on the muddy sides of retaining walls, the appearance of species such as *Tussilago farfara*, *Chenopodium rubrum*, *Rumex crispus*, *R. obtusifolius*, *Tripleurospermum maritimum*, *Plantago lanceolata*, *P. major*, and species of ubiquitous weedy genera such as *Polygonum*, *Atriplex*, *Cirsium* and *Equisetum*, is a possibility. Likely candidates for the waterlogged, unaerated areas include *Ranunculus sceleratus*, *Bidens tripartita*, *B. cernua*, *Polygonum amphibium*, *Juncus inflexus*, *Scirpus tabernaemontani* and *Aster tripolium*. This sort of association, with a halophytic element, can be seen at present fringing the Cheshire salt 'flashes' at Winsford or Sandbach. Certain of these pioneers may persist as troublesome weeds, as have *Tussilago farfara* and *Cirsium arvense* in the Dutch polders (Bakker 1960b).

Subsequently the pioneer species may be replaced by the upward spread of reedswamp or rush species, or be ousted by the arrival of sward-forming species such as *Agrostis stolonifera* or *Alopecurus geniculatus. Agrostis stolonifera* may be a particularly important species. Preliminary experiments have indicated that it can withstand up to six months total immersion in winter. The rate of clonal expansion of *A. stolonifera* pioneers on newly exposed mud is very high, and it has formed a dense, almost pure mat, covering a large area of the Quoile lake edge. It will colonise wet rotavated marshland soil to give almost complete cover within one year (Ranwell, personal communication).

The fact that species such as *Agrostis stolonifera* are already present in the intertidal marshland which is to be submerged adds a further complication to the task of predicting changes. For, aside from any invasion by plants from nearby habitats, these *in situ* species have an important ecological advantage, namely possession and, providing the rate at which the environment changes does not exceed the rate at which they can adapt to it by the plastic modification of individuals, this advantage could prove a telling one. However there are difficulties in predicting which species may be important in this respect. In order to do so detailed information of their distribution and biology is required for all the species involved. It is when one starts to collect this that the difficulties become apparent. An example from current studies on the Morecambe Bay flora may serve to illustrate this point.

The saltmarshes of Morecambe Bay are characterised by the dominance of grasses at most stages of the succession. *Puccinellia maritima*, *Festuca rubra* and *Agrostis stolonifera* are the most abundant species in the swards above Mean High Water Spring Tides. Their differential distribution in relation to altitude, substrate, sheep grazing and commercial turf cutting, suggests that a complex balance of factors determines which species succeeds at a given site. *Puccinellia* is the primary colonist in most areas, being present as isolated clumps in the lower zones, and rising to a pure sward. This is eventually replaced by a hummocky sward with *Festuca* on the well drained hummocks and *Puccinellia* in the poorly drained, muddier hollows. The *Festuca/Armeria maritima* sward above this association contains, with increasing altitude, an increasing number of individuals of *Agrostis* until this latter species becomes codominant. The *Festuca/Agrostis* sward is succeeded by associations dominated by *Juncus gerardii* and *J. maritimus* in that order. This pattern, with minor variations in the presence of associated species (notably *Parapholis strigosa*, *Plantago maritima* and *Triglochin maritima*) is repeated in most of the saltmarshes from Hest Bank to the Leven estuary. However in the mid-estuary of the R. Kent *Agrostis* appears before *Festuca* in the *Puccinellia* sward and, in the upper estuary, takes over the role of pioneer. In addition, *Festuca* and *Agrostis* have a more obviously differential distribution on these estuarine marshes, the former being restricted to creek levees (with *Agropyron pungens* and *Festuca arundinacea*) and the latter to hollows such as the sites of former pans or creeks (a niche which it shares with *Scirpus maritimus* and *Alopecurus geniculatus*). The areas laid bare by the removal of turves are invaded mainly by *Agrostis* or *Puccinellia* or both, depending on the level at which the cutting is exposed although *Puccinellia* is found up to 3 feet above its normal upper limit in the pioneer sward.

Preliminary greenhouse experiments have indicated that *Puccinellia* is more tolerant of saline conditions than either of the other two species although all three showed some tolerance. Hannon and Bradshaw (1968) concluded that the restriction of *Agrostis* to upper marsh levels was not due to any inability to evolve as high a degree of salt tolerance as that of *Festuca*. Our own experiments have indicated that under competition-free conditions, there is no significant difference in the mean dry weight of individuals of the maritime *Festuca* grown under four different levels of waterlogging (varying from lightly watered plants to those grown with a permanent water table at soil level). In these experiments seedlings were grown for up to four months in garden soils. However under all conditions of waterlogging in nutrient poor sands the growth of mature tillers of *Festuca* was increasingly depressed by competition with themselves, *Puccinellia* tillers and *Agrostis* tillers in that order, *Agrostis* depressing growth the most. *Puccinellia* was highly tolerant of complete waterlogging and suffered some depression of growth in competition with *Agrostis* in lightly watered soils. *Agrostis* competed favourably with the other two species in a series of mixtures under all conditions, but was relatively less successful (in terms of top dry weight) in competition with *Festuca* in lightly watered conditions.

The variation of these three species alone in relation to variation in conditions of competition, soil type, the age of the plant, waterlogging and salinity, reveals a complex of interacting factors any one of which may, in the event, swing the balance. One may ask whether the initial high salinities of the estuarine muds will enable the salt-tolerant *Puccinellia* to spread to an extent that it can dominate the waterlogged areas created during the gradual filling of the reservoir? Or perhaps the apparent competitive advantage of *Agrostis* under waterlogged conditions will enable it to oust both *Festuca* and *Puccinellia* from their former zones of dominance? It would be naive to assume that the situation is as simple as even this but, faced with a plethora of possibilities, we may be starting to ask the right sort of questions. Refining the questions is the first step towards designing the relevant experiments.

I have dealt only with the short-term colonisation of exposed and shallowly submerged land on the reservoir margins. The invasion of deeper water, of the exposed high level saltmarshes, and of any newly accreted intertidal land can equally be the subject of interesting conjecture. It is perhaps worth inviting botanists to allow themselves, privately and without fear of reputation, the indulgence of naming their favourites. It should certainly be a fascinating exercise to compare the lists of likely species drawn up by different field botanists.

The type of information required

Until such time as we can monitor an actual example how are we to anticipate how individual species will react? Detailed information relating to germination and dispersal biology, of the sort which Harper and his co-workers have provided for certain of the species such as *Rumex crispus* (Cavers and Harper 1964), is needed for all the species likely to be important. This, together with a detailed inventory of the location and size of the local populations prior to any changes, is a very first requirement.

We then need information as to the likely season and duration of periods of drawdown in order to assess whether there could be any appreciable growth of ephemerals on the temporarily exposed areas. We need to learn of the effects of the estuarine reservoir on the water-table and drainage of the hinterland, and on the local micro-climate. This sort of information, together with predictions of the likely pattern of silting seaward of the barrage, is available to some extent from the engineers and from large-scale model studies. From the soil chemist we need to learn of the possible consequences of the death of intertidal organisms, and of algal 'blooms' on the nutrient status of the exposed mud-flats which were significant aspects of the ripening of newly exposed soils in Holland. Having obtained all this information it is dangerous to assume that all species will be adequate to occupy the niches suitable to them. On the contrary, what documented information is available suggests that, in newly created areas, there is a tendency towards the development of large pure stands of a few individual species. The mosaic of micro-habitat variation which maintains a delicate balance between a large number of species in, for example, a natural mixed fen, rarely has time to develop in these uniform areas. The trend away from richness towards uniformity is further reinforced by the chance availability of ecologically suitable seed parents. Those species with a high reproductive capacity or rate of spread which happen to arrive first in the new niche may occupy it to the exclusion of their competitors with similar properties, but which invade at a later stage.

It is equally dangerous to assume that the arrival of the colonists or the anticipated purity of the initial stands will be an evanescent phenomenon creating new niches by classical seral processes. Moyle and Nielson (1953) report that, on the drained basins of several lakes in northern Minnesota, successions were often disorderly and accelerated due to the rapidity of changes in the physical and chemical environment associated with the soil drainage.

We are left, it seems, very much in the sort of position which Professor Webb's treatment of the subject of Dispersal and Establishment left us in an earlier Conference (Webb 1966)—in ignorance of essential basic information and without an adequate calculus of probabilities. For, even were the basic information available, we may be required to balance, for example, the seed output and high germination rate of some species *(Rumex crispus)* against the rapid vegetative spread but low germination rate of others *(Scirpus maritimus)*.

Conclusions

The building of barrages represents only one of a number of threats to estuarine areas which are, in any event, highly sensitive systems (Ranwell 1968). The scale of the proposed operations and the fundamental changes which they will bring about can scarcely leave the British flora unaffected. It will be interesting to discover, if and when these schemes mature, whether man's imprint increases the weedy, invasive component of our flora. Part of the message implied above is that this may not necessarily be the case. It may be that, incidentally, we provide niches for ecologically restricted species such as *Ranunculus sceleratus*, extend the range of those with local distributions such as *Rumex palustris* or *Rumex maritimus* or even allow species such as *Senecio palustris*, now extinct, to return.

Whilst on this theme may I return finally to the second of my two earlier assumptions. It was, in effect, the supposition that the present ecological behaviour of a given species is an entirely reliable guide to its reaction to new situations. This ignores the ability of the local species population to adapt, by phenotypic plasticity or by longer-term genetic divergence, to produce types suitable to newly created situations. It is in just such highly dynamic environments that the conditions for divergence, and even speciation, are at an optimum. Taxa such as the hybrid *Typha*, reported from America by Harris and Marshall (1963) to have a faster rate of spread and a greater tolerance of fluctuating water levels than either of its parents, could conceivably become widespread. Botanists can certainly ill afford to regard such areas as unnatural and, by implication, 'spoiled' and unworthy of their attentions. It may be that there, to misquote Yeats, its hour come at last, a rough beast is waiting to be born.

REFERENCES

ANON. (1966a). *Solway Barrage*. H.M.S.O., London.

ANON. (1966b). *Morecambe Bay Barrage*. H.M.S.O., London.

ANON. (1966c). *Morecambe Bay and Solway Barrages*. H.M.S.O., London.

BAKKER, D. (1960a). *Senecio congestus* (R.Br.) DC. in the Lake Yssel polders. *Act. Bot. Neerl.* **9**, 235-259.

BAKKER, D. (1960b). A comparative life-history study of *Cirsium arvense* (L.) Scop. and *Tussilago farfara* L., the most troublesome weeds in the newly reclaimed polders of the former Zuiderzee. In Harper, J.L. (Ed.) (1960).

BAKKER, D., JONKER, J. J. and SMITS, H. (1960). Land reclamation in Holland. *Shell Public Health and Agricultural News* **3**, 143-151.

CAVERS, P. B. and HARPER, J. L. (1964). Biological Flora of the British Isles. *Rumex obtusifolius* L. and *R. crispus* L. *J. Ecol.* **52**, 737-766.

GILSON, H. C. (1966). The biological implications of the proposed barrages across Morecambe Bay and the Solway Firth. In Lowe-McConnell, R. H. (Ed.) (1966).

HANNON, N. and BRADSHAW, A. D. (1968). Evolution of salt tolerance in two coexisting species of grass. *Nature, Lond.* **220**, 1342-3.

HARPER, J. L. (Ed.) (1960). *The Biology of Weeds.* Oxford.

HARRIS, S. W. and MARSHALL, W. H. (1963). Ecology of water-level manipulations on a northern marsh. *Ecology* **44**, 331-343.

HAWKES, J. G. (Ed.) (1966). *Reproductive Biology and Taxonomy of Vascular Plants.* Oxford & London.

INGLIS, C. C. and KESTNER, F. J. T. (1958). The long-term effects of training walls, reclamation and dredging on estuaries. *Proc. Instn. Civ. Engrs* **9**, 193-216.

KESTNER, F. J. T. (1961). Short-term changes in the distribution of fine sediments in estuaries. *Proc. Instn. Civ. Engrs* **19**, 185-208.

KESTNER, F. J. T. (1962). The old coastline of the Wash. *Geog. J.* **128**, 457-478.

KESTNER, F. J. T. and INGLIS C. C. (1956). A study of erosion and accretion during cyclic changes in an estuary and their effect on reclamation of marginal land. *J. Agric. Eng. Res.* **1**, 63-67.

LOWE-McCONNELL, R. H. (Ed.) (1966). *Man-made Lakes.* (Proc. Symp. Inst. Biol. 15.) London & New York.

MOYLE, J. B. and NIELSEN, E. L. (1953). Further observation on forest invasion and succession on basins of drained lakes in northern Minnesota. *Am. Midl. Nat.* **50**, 805-821.

RANWELL, D. S. (1968). Coastal marshes in perspective. *University of Strathclyde Regional Studies Group Bulletin* **9**, 1-26.

WEBB, D. A. (1966). Dispersal and establishment: what do we really know? In Hawkes, J. G. (Ed.) (1966). 93-102.

DISCUSSION

Dr D. H. DALBY said that some guide to the development of the early stages of saltmarshes under brackish water conditions could be gained from the Baltic. He was convinced that colonisation of the areas of accretion outside the barrage would be rapid. A factor of great importance in predicting colonisation of saltmarshes was the presence of *Spartinaxanglica*. Previous natural saltmarsh formation had taken place before this species arrived: but it is now available for colonising in most areas. He then asked Mr. Gray whether the line of the proposed barrage in Morecambe Bay had yet been settled.

Mr GRAY replied that it had not. One line being considered stretched from north of Morecambe to Aldingham. Pump storage schemes were also being considered in the Silverdale area.

Mr H. H. LAMB said that large bodies of freshwater produced by barrages might alter the thermal character of an area by natural and artificial means. The substitution of land-derived and land-locked water for water connected to the sea could cause an increase in the fluctuation of temperatures from week to week, though probably the annual mean would not alter. The temperature could be altered artificially if the area attracted industry. In the winter of 1962 it was discovered that the city of London raised the temperature of the R. Thames from Kingston to the mouth of the Medway by 10°C.

Mr R. M. BURTON asked whether the Morecambe Bay barrage would affect species on Humphrey Head which are probably dependent on their proximity to the sea for survival.

Mr GRAY replied that if the barrage removed the sea about 500m from Humphrey Head then halophytes like *Crithmum maritimum* would probably be replaced by *Festuca rubra*.

Dr D. A. RATCLIFFE said that other frost sensitive species like *Adiantum capillus-veneris* might also be affected.

Mr C. J. JEFFEREY asked how much saltmarsh species depended upon the gradual mixing of salt and fresh water. What could be the effect of creating a sudden break, could saltmarsh species colonise the area of accretion.?

Mr GRAY thought that this was a most difficult question to answer until the exact condition of the new habitat were known.

Mr E. MILNE-REDHEAD asked how much fresh water would pass out to sea.

Mr GRAY said the amount would be small. The lake was unlikely to be full for long: the biological interest would be in studying the effect of drawdown, rather than overflow.

THE INFLUENCE OF TRANSPORT ON
A CHANGING FLORA

J. E. LOUSLEY

Introduction

From the dawn of history transport has exercised a major influence on the British flora. The construction and use of tracks, roads, canals, railways and airports has involved many changes—some direct, and others indirect. It is my purpose to provide a broad outline of this neglected subject rather than to give detailed examples.

The direct influences include the destruction of existing habitats and the provision of new ones made by man which have special characteristics. These have provided more or less continuous stretches of open habitats extending for hundreds of miles and forming a nation-wide network, with opportunities for rapid colonisation and spread such as rarely occur in nature. The story of the advantage taken of these networks by a few alien species is well known but no serious attempt has been made to study their effect on "native" plants.

The indirect influence of transport is too big a subject to permit consideration here. I must, however, point out that the opening up of new facilities inevitably promotes economic developments of great importance to botanists. Just as the construction of railways opened up the prairie provinces of Canada, so transport improvements have been followed by the agricultural and commercial exploitation of the areas they served in Britain. These changes in agriculture carried seeds, many of them foreign, about the country to grow in new places. The transport of building materials has facilitated the destruction of vegetation by the construction of towns and factories in some places with materials dug out of the ground in others. Without transport the exploitation of Britain would have remained local and limited, and our flora would have been very different.

Tracks and roads

Large-volume long-distance land transport is a very recent development, but from the earliest times there were tracks round villages. As now, these would encourage the spread of species like *Bellis perennis*, *Plantago major*, and *Polygonum aviculare* which can endure trampling and compacted soils and require freedom from the competition of taller plants. The work of Godwin and others has built up a considerable record of the increase of such species related to the activities of prehistoric man. As Westhoff (1967) has recently pointed out, tracks also open up a broad swathe which lets light into dense communities and favours the growth and extension of some less common species along their sides. Longer distance tracks, such as those over downs and moorland, tended to spread out, and thus provided wide areas of trampled, rutted or disturbed ground. Only 200 years ago goods were still carried by long strings of pack-horses in some parts of the country. Cattle were driven long distances on the drove roads from Scotland, Wales and northern England to markets in the south, and turkeys from Norfolk to London. Seeds and fruits would be carried attached to the animals and others would pass through them to be excreted further along the route.

It was not until late in the 18th century that long stretches of reasonable roads were available for coaches and wagons. For the coaches alone it has been estimated that by the 1830s some 150,000 horses were required (Copeland 1968, p. 284) and the total number for all road traffic must have been very high indeed. The consequent demand for pastures and hayfields was heavily reduced with the introduction of railways. This helps to explain the loss of plants of permanent pastures at this period.

The framework of practical trunk roads made possible by the surfacing methods of John Loudon McAdam (1756-1836) and others encouraged the provision of a network of secondary roads and facilitated local transport. People now came out of the towns into the country, and whereas attractive species had previously suffered only the limited depredations of the villagers, they were now subject to picking and uprooting on a much larger scale. My ancestor Job Lousley, in a remote village on the Berkshire Downs, was bemoaning this before the middle of last century (Lousley 1964), and from small beginnings there has built up a threat to our flora of major proportions. Many of us can recall the weekend return journey to large towns of hundreds of cyclists loaded with primroses, bluebells, wild daffodils, and other attractive flowers. Widespread ownership of cars increased their range and carrying capacity, and the circles of devastation round our large towns have steadily increased as roads became better and cars became relatively cheaper. They are still growing.

Roadside verges offer a sanctuary for plants and until recently they were free from human disturbance other than the grazing of cottagers' animals. They have been especially valuable in limestone areas where, as for example in Lincolnshire, they sometimes provided the only relics of ancient turf. During recent years the width of verges generally has been greatly reduced and I now seldom see the broad flowery stretches with which I was familiar in my youth—road widening has been the main reason for the loss. Nevertheless a recent estimate suggests that they still total some 171,000 acres in England and Wales and provide habitats for over 700 species of flowering plants. (Perring 1967).

TABLE I

Mileage of Public Roads in Great Britain 1967

	Miles
Motorway	416
Trunk	8,377
Principal (mainly Class 1) ..	20,221
Other	173,660
Total	202,674

Source: *Annual Abstract of Statistics* 1968, Table 231.

Valuable though they still are, the character of roadside verges has changed considerably. Fifty years ago most roads, even quite important ones, had a loose and dusty surface with the sides flanked with a strip of disturbed ground where annuals, and especially agricultural weeds, were plentiful. The general adoption of asphalt, concrete, and other forms of hard surface, has resulted in an abrupt change to coarse and mainly perennial vegetation. Verges are now subject to much more disturbance from the laying of gas and electric mains, telephone cables and sewers, and this disturbance is often shown by the presence of coarse grasses such as *Arrhenatherum elatius* and *Dactylis glomerata*. The requirements of modern transport necessitate, or are supposed to necessitate, frequent mowing or spraying with herbicides of various types. It is fortunate that Naturalists' Trusts are now recording, and collaborating with County Surveyors in protecting, selected stretches of roadside verges. Modern motorways present rather different problems and will be discussed separately.

Water transport

The history of canals in Britain dates from 1758 when the Duke of Bridgewater obtained statutory powers for the construction of an artificial waterway from Worley Mill to Salford. By 1830 the network of canals was virtually complete. From Kendal and York in the north there was a continuous chain of navigable rivers and canals to London and the south coast. From Liverpool, Llangollen, Newtown (Montgomeryshire), Hay, Brecknock, Gloucester and Bristol in the west, continuous fresh water extended east to the Humber, Boston and London. The effect on our aquatic flora must have been dramatic. Previously these plants could only extend into new habitats by transfer of seed or fragments through the air. Now small scraps caught up on barges were dragged under water for miles to reach new places where the use and maintenance of the canals enabled them to become established with little immediate competition. Moreover the barges took them upstream as well as down.

One well documented early example arises from aspects of the dramatic spread of Canadian waterweed, *Elodea canadensis*. This was first found in England in 1846 in storage reservoirs by Foxton Locks on the canal near Market Harborough, Leicestershire. This canal was then only 30 years old and, from evidence of a locksman, it seems that the plant had been there for about 20 years. The place was virtually the centre of the new network and records soon came in from other canals in the Midlands. In 1852 Marshall described this early spread and said that the plant was extending into connected rivers. He pointed out that it was well placed to extend throughout the inland waterways system and his forecast was soon fulfilled. In Ireland *Elodea canadensis* appeared in a pond about 1836, and some eight years later it was in the Lagan Canal near Lisburn, Co. Antrim. The Lagan and two other canals were joined through Lough Neagh and it is not surprising that the plant was soon in these other canals. (Walker 1911).

Canadian waterweed was well recorded because it was easily recognised, had economic significance and received a great deal of publicity. No doubt many native aquatics spread rapidly during the early history of canals but their spread attracted little attention. More recently *Elatine hydropiper* has extended from its natural habitat in Lough Neagh along the Newry and Lagan Canals. In England, *Luronium natans* and *Callitriche hermaphroditica* are an indication of what took place. Their natural habitats are rather acid lakes in mountainous districts from which they have been brought down to the lowlands. The distribution of Potamogetons owes a great deal to the chain of periodically cleaned waterways which extended the range of species, and brought them into contact with other species so that hybrids arose.

Canals also provided a type of artificial habitat rare in Britain: stretches of heated water with little variation in temperature throughout the year. In the "hot lodges", where water used for cooling in the Lancashire mills was discharged into canals, exotic aquatics such as *Naias graminea*, *Vallisneria spiralis*, and *Egeria densa* were able to persist. Canals offered not only continuous freshwater habitats but also the disturbed ground on the towpaths which was continuous for hundreds of miles except for occasional switching from one side of the water to the other. I watched the spread of *Juncus tenuis* along the towpath of the Basingstoke Canal in Surrey some forty years ago and there must have been many other examples.

The use and maintenance of canals has now been in decline for a century, and great as has been their influence in the past they are unlikely to affect our flora very much in the future. The British Waterways Board took over 2000 miles of inland waterways in 1963, but of these some 500 miles were already formally "closed to navigation" and a further 600 miles were no longer used by commercial traffic. Only 400 miles, carrying 90% of the total traffic, were classified as of major transport use and most of these, contaminated with oil and subject to the wash of motor barges, would be unfavourable to aquatics. The old conditions of a controlled flow of slowly moving water, regular dredging and horse-drawn barges are gone for ever and the botanical interest of most of the remaining canals is rapidly declining.

In addition to the waterways themselves the canal system needed storage reservoirs to maintain a regular flow of water— the Welsh Harp at Hendon and Tring Reservoirs are examples. In these the water-level fluctuated widely and in the summer large areas of sandy mud were often exposed for long periods. These provided important habitats for mud ephemerals such as *Limosella aquatica* and *Chenopodium rubrum* and some continue to do so.

Water transport still remains the principle means by which bulky goods are imported from overseas and vast numbers of foreign seeds enter this country daily through the docks as impurities in grain, wool and other cargoes. In the past these yielded a rich harvest to botanists interested in aliens. Adventives were numerous at the larger docks, and especially Avonmouth, Cardiff, Barry, Gloucester, Southampton, Colchester, Felixstowe, Manchester, Hull and Leith. They also were found at small quays such as those on some of the East Anglian creeks, and formerly on ballast hills, especially in south Wales and north-east England where ships engaged in the export of minerals returned to this country with foreign soil as ballast. Now there is very little to be found in association with shipping. Soil is no longer used as ballast, the small quays are abandoned as uneconomic, while the larger docks are kept almost free from weeds. Whereas formerly grain, oil seeds and some other cargoes were unloaded loose into railway wagons which went off dribbling weed seeds on to the track to grow and possibly spread, the new mechanical methods of handling ensure that there is little or no spillage. The modern use of containers which are packed at source and not opened until they reach their destination will still further reduce the chances of plants spreading from our ports. Shipping will continue to bring foreign seeds to Britain but any dissemination will be from the inland places of delivery and very much more difficult to study.

Railways

The first public railway bill was presented to Parliament in 1801 and by 1825 there were 418 miles of railway. This increased to 52,567 miles of track in 1928. In recent years closures, and especially those under the Beeching Plan have reduced the mileage by about a third—from 52,003 miles in 1950 to 34,498 at the end of 1967. These closures still continue.

The immediate effect of the construction of railways was the destruction of existing habitats and the creation of new ones. There were major alterations in drainage, so that bogs and marshes were lost or altered, and there was general disturbance along a broad strip on both sides of the line. Embankments and cuttings were created offering new well drained habitats on slopes, and material excavated was sometimes left piled up in long heaps which persist to this day. On the track itself a continuous strip of ballast offered a new habitat favourable to thermo-xerophilous communities. This, with the disturbed ground on each side, formed a continuous ribbon throughout the railway network all over Britain. It even extended through the built-up centres of towns. It is regrettable that no attempt has been made to reconstruct from the botanical records of the 19th century the effect on our flora of the construction of railways. Neither has any general study been made of the ecology of the very special habitats which were created. The differences between north- and south-, east- and west-facing embankments and cuttings, between those on different rocks and soil and in different parts of the country, or on railways in use for different types of traffic, offer a rich field for study. It is seldom that botanists are offered a series of habitats which can be dated so precisely, where the management history is known, and which present so many contrasts.

Useful, though limited, studies of railway floras have been carried out by Almquist in Sweden, Wiinstedt in Denmark, Mikkola in Finland, Muehlenbach on the St. Louis network in the U.S.A., Jovet on the Paris Metro, and recently by Messenger in Rutland. There is a characteristic railway flora in which many species are the same in all these northern temperate countries. In Britain the part played by railways in the spread of *Senecio squalidus* is familiar and has been described in detail by Kent. Other species which have found a favourable habitat on the ballast of the permanent way, sidings and tracksides include *Cochlearia danica*, *Cerastium diffusum (atrovirens)*, *Corrigiola litoralis*, *Sedum acre*, *Chaenorhinum minus* and *Senecio viscosus*. The spread of maritime species may have been initiated by ballast brought from the coast. On the embankments, *Diplotaxis tenuifolia*, *Cheiranthus cheiri*, *Dianthus barbatus*, *Geranium pyrenaicum*, *Colutea arborescens*, *Epilobium angustifolium*, *Antirrhinum majus*, various *Hieracia*, and *Chrysanthemum leucanthemum* are familiar examples of species which have spread along railways.

One rather surprising aspect is the part played by railways in the distribution of ferns. Moist railway brickwork, and especially that under north-facing platforms, or where steam engines were regularly checked at signals, provide conditions favourable for the development of fern prothalli. Thus *Cystopteris fragilis* has spread from its native haunts in the north and west to the brickwork of railways (and canals) in the lowlands of the south-east and East Anglia. *Ceterach officinarum*, characteristically a western fern, is found in many places on railways in the east. *Adiantum capillus-veneris* thrives on railway brickwork, sometimes from spores of native plants as at Bandon, Co. Cork, but probably more often from greenhouse plants. The occurrence of these ferns outside their normal distribution have attracted attention, but many more widespread species have had their spores carried in the currents behind express trains to found new colonies along the line.

Another aspect is the introduction of weeds, and sometimes

from seeds of foreign origin. Workers who helped with the Maps Scheme, and especially those who worked in Ireland, will recall how easy it was after spending a day in a square which was floristically poor, to boost up the numbers by visiting the sidings at country railway stations. The rich harvest of wool aliens found formerly at sidings in Bedfordshire and Yorkshire are familiar examples of the part railways played in the distribution of foreign seeds. It is evident that the handling of large quantities of straw, hay, grain and other produce at several thousand country stations throughout Britain for over a century offered scope for considerable movement of native plants as well as aliens.

Railways are likely to have very much less influence on our flora in the future. As already mentioned, lines are still being closed and sidings removed. In 1957 British Railways had 2,352 freight stations; in 1967 only 729. Most country stations no longer handle goods. On tracks still in use the main lines are being developed as Inter-City routes maintained to a very high standard. Weed-killers keep the permanent way free from vegetation except for a few resistant species like *Corrigiola*. The old management regime of cutting and firing the embankments is being changed so that their value as refuges for locally uncommon plants (such as the primrose in built-up areas) is reduced. It is expected that on some lines most trains will soon travel at well over a hundred miles an hour. The strong air currents set up by these increased speeds may have interesting effects on the transport of fruits and on vegetation in narrow cuttings.

On the remaining branch lines the botanical outlook is better, though even here the spraying of the permanent way with herbicides from special trucks is so easy that few plants are allowed to grow on the permanent way. When lines are eventually abandoned they are invaded remarkably quickly by the more aggressive species from adjacent areas and are often rapidly overgrown with scrub. For a short time these are of great interest but, like canals, railways lose their special characteristics very soon after use and maintenance ceases. It is fortunate that some Naturalists' Trusts have been able to arrange for the necessary maintenance to conserve a few miles of special interest.

Motorways and trunk roads

It will be seen from Table II that the tonnage of goods transported by road in Britain is already over seven times as much as by rail, while the figure for inland waterways is almost insignificant. This tendency is being accelerated by the construction of motorways and the improvement of trunk roads to provide much faster journeys. They also provide conditions for plants very different from those of the old roads. By the end of 1967 there were 416 miles of motorway but these are being increased rapidly, and many of the 8,377 miles of trunk roads have been improved or reconstructed to new alignments on modern standards.

The construction of new roads must inevitably cause some

TABLE II

Goods Transport in Great Britain in 1967

In tons			Million tons
Road	..	.. ..	1,500
Rail ..	..	.. ..	201
Coastal Shipping	..	..	52
Inland Waterways	..	..	7
Pipelines	..	.. ..	27
Total goods transport		..	1,787

In ton miles			Thousand million
Road	..	.. ..	73·2
Rail ..	..	.. ..	43·0

Source: *Annual Abstract of Statistics* 1968, Table 229.

destruction of habitats but so far serious loss has not been extensive·
The indirect results of dividing farms and estates, with resulting
changes in the management of the less accessible parts, may prove
to have a greater effect on our flora. As with railways, the new
fast motor-roads create new habitats with their cuttings and embankments but, unlike railways, are commonly planted (see p. 84).
Standard grass mixtures, partly of foreign origin, are often used,
and these seem to explain the rather frequent occurence of the
graceful grass *Hordeum jubatum*. They are also likely to be the
origin of *Senecio vernalis* which was first found by Mrs. M. Tulloh
in Devon in 1961.

It is very difficult to gain access to the embankments on motorways and they cannot be properly observed at the speeds cars
commonly travel at. This is unfortunate since, in the early stages,
they provide a series of continuous more or less open habitats.
On these, introductions from planting and seeding could travel fast
and unobserved.

Air transport

I have been unable to find evidence that the growing volume
of air transport has had, or is likely to have, any significant influence
on the British flora. The wheels of aircraft operating from prepared
runways are usually free from mud and any seeds attached at the
moment of take-off would be quickly removed by the tremendous
air friction before the wheels are retracted in the undercarriage.
It may be that fruits occasionally float into the cabins but the
chances are small and they would have to survive the air conditioning
system before they could float out again at the end of their journey.
It is much more likely that seeds get conveyed on the clothing of
passengers, and especially on those old-fashioned enough to have

turn-ups to their trousers.   In view of the way passengers are dealt with at airports such seeds would usually be carried miles away before they were released in a suitable place for germination.

There are a few, a very few, cases in which air transport has been suspected as the source of aliens.   One such was at the American war-time airbase at Greenham in Berkshire but *Ononis natrix* and other foreign plants found there were probably introduced with materials or grain not necessarily imported by air.   Airports do, however, form a useful sanctuary for plants although the construction of new ones may destroy areas of botanical interest.

The future

I have endeavoured to summarise the influence which transport has had on the British flora in the past.   This reached its maximum in the 19th century when the construction of canals and railways destroyed many habitats and created new networks along which plants were able to spread.   The unrestricted import of foreign plants as impurities in agricultural seed and commodities, and the general tolerance of weeds favoured rapid spread.   There was an accelerating trend towards greater and more rapid disturbance and, as engineering skills increased, towards more traffic and faster speeds on the roads.   In the present century the change from horse to motor traction has brought many changes in the transport system.

In future the influence of the very restricted network of remaining canals can only be slight.   Cleaner conditions, herbicides, and the use of "containers" will greatly restrict the chances of establishment of foreign plants in and near the docks.   Railways will continue to influence our flora but their role will be greatly reduced by the closure of track, disuse and removal of sidings, centralisation and reduction of freight, chemical spraying of tracks, and high standards of maintenance on Inter-City routes.   There is no evidence that aircraft will have any considerable influence, though new airfields will destroy existing habitats and create new ones (as perhaps at Foulness), and hovercraft may cause disturbance from turbulence.

Trackways, roads and motorways are likely to influence our flora more than any of these.   Trackways, in spite of the loss of country footpaths, will continue to provide special habitats and distribution routes for some species which endure trampling, and open up closed habitats for others.   Roads will still provide verges and temporary open habitats.   Motorways are a new feature of which we have little experience.   They have considerable potential for destruction when they are built, but may well provide opportunities for the spread of new plants.   The future influence of transport may be less than it has been in the past, but it will still be considerable.

REFERENCES

ALLEN, D. E. (1962).   Railway colonists in the Isle of Man.   *Proc. bot. Soc. Br. Isl.* **4,** 502.

ALLEN, G. F. (1966).   *British Rail after Beeching*.   London.

ALMQUIST, ERIK (1957). Järnsvägsfloristiska notiser. *Svensk bot. Tidskr.* **51**, 223-263.

Annual Abstract of Statistics **105**. (1968). H.M.S.O., London.

BOUBY, H. (1962). Notes détachées sur la flore parisienne (6-8). *Cah. Nat.* **18**, 27-30.

BRITISH RAILWAYS BOARD (1963). *The Reshaping of British Railways* [Beeching Report]. H.M.S.O., London.

BRITISH WATERWAYS BOARD (1964). *The Future of the Waterways.* H.M.S.O., London.

BRITISH WATERWAYS BOARD (1965). *The Facts about the Waterways.* H.M.S.O., London.

BRITISH WATERWAYS BOARD (1967). *Leisure and the Waterways.* H.M.S.O., London.

CARPENTER, K. and WILSON, C. (1954). The use of 2, 4-D and 2,4,5-T brush-killers on railway embankments. *Proc. Br. Weed Control Conf.* 2nd, 523-533.

CARTER, E. F. (1959). *An Historical Geography of the Railways of the British Isles.* London.

CHRISTIAN, G. (1964). When nature takes over the railways. *Ctry Life* **135**, 1642-1643.

CLARK, M. C. (1964). [Plants introduced with sea-sand on a railway]. *Proc. Bgham nat. Hist. phil. Soc.* **20**, 37.

COPELAND, John (1968). *Roads & their Traffic*, 1750-1850. London.

DHIEN, R. (1967). Un peuplement initial de végétation [Colonisation of a disused railway]. *Revue Féd. fr. Soc. Sci. nat.* **6**, 3-8.

DICKIE, G. (1854). On the occurrence of *Anacharis alsinastrum* in Ireland. *The Phytologist* **5**, 88.

DICKIE, G. (1864). *Flora of Ulster.* Belfast.

ELLIS, C. H. (1954 & 1959). *British Railway History.* 2 vols. London.

GRIGSON, Geoffrey (1952). Flowers & Men. *History Today* **2**, 823-831.

HADFIELD, E. C. R. (1959). *British Canals: an illustrated history.* Ed. 2. London.

JACKMAN, W. T. (1966). *The Development of Transportation in Modern England.* Ed. 3. London.

JOVET, P. (1940). Remarques sur l'introduction et la propagation de quelques plantes par les voies de communication. *C.r. somm Séanc. Soc. Biogéogr.* **17** (145), 29-34.

JOVET, P. (1945). Vegetation des lignes aeriennes du chemin de fer metro-politain de Paris. *Bull. Soc. bot. Fr.* **92**, 92-97 & 105-109.

KENT, D. H. (1960). *Senecio squalidus* L. in the British Isles. 2. The spread from Oxford (1879-1939). *Proc. bot. Soc. Br. Isl.* **3**, 375-379.

LOUSLEY, J. E. (1964). The Berkshire records of Job Lousley (1790-1855). *Proc. bot. Soc. Br. Isl.* **5**, 203-209.

MARSHALL, W. (1852). Excessive and noxious increase of *Udora canadensis (Anacharis alsinastrum)*. *The Phytologist* **4**, 705-715.

MESSENGER, K. G. (1968). A Railway Flora of Rutland. *Proc. bot. Soc. Br. Isl.* **7**, 325-344.

MIKKOLA, R. (1966). Ratakasvihavaintoja Siitamen ja Lylyn seudulta (Orivesi, Kangasla ja Juupajoki, Ta). *Memo. Soc. Fauna Flora fenn.* **42**, 14-26.

MUEHLENBACH, V. (1969). Along the railroad tracks: a study of adventive plants. *Bull. Mo. bot. Gdn* **57**, 10-18.

NEWMAN, E. (1847a). Occurrence of *Udora canadensis*, a plant new to Britain and Europe, near Market Harborough, in Leicestershire. *The Phytologist* **2**, 1050.

NEWMAN, E. (1847b). *Udora canadensis*? *The Phytologist* **2**, x-xiii.

NIEMI, A. (1969). On the railway vegetation and flora between Esbo and Inga, S. Finland. *Acta bot. fenn.* **83**, 1-28.

PEDERSEN, A. (1955). Indslaebte planter ved jernbanerne. *Flora Fauna Silkeborg* **61**, 81-109.
PERRING, F. H. (1967). Verges are Vital—A Botanist looks at our Roadsides. *J. Instn Highw. Engrs* **14**, 13-16.
PRAEGER, R. L. and MEGAW, W. R. (1938). *Flora of the North-east of Ireland.* Ed. 2. Belfast.
RYAN, H. J. (1929). Airplanes a means for disseminating noxious weed seeds. *Mon. Bull. Calif. Dep. Agric.* **18**, 245.
SAVIDGE, J. P. (Ed.) (1963). *Travis's Flora of South Lancashire.* Liverpool.
SCULTHORPE, C. D. (1967). *The Biology of Aquatic Plants.* London.
SHAW, C. E. (1963). Canals. In Savidge, J. P. (Ed.) (1963).
STEWART, S. A. and CORRY, T. H. (1888). *Flora of the North-east of Ireland.* Cambridge.
SWINSCOW, T. D. V. (1955). Ferns on a railway platform. *Proc. bot. Soc. Br. Isl.* **1**, 392.
VALLEI, F. G. (1967). "Legeradventieven" te Harskamp. *Gorteria* **3**, 130-131.
WALKER, A. O. (1912). The distribution of *Elodea canadensis* Michaux in the British Isles in 1909. *Proc. Linn. Soc. Lond.* **124**, 71-77.
WALTERS, S. M. (1969). Cambridgeshire ferns—ecclesiastic and ferroviatic. *Nature Cambs.* **12**, 22-25.
WESTHOFF, V. (1967). The ecological impact of pedestrian, equestrian and vehicular traffic on vegetation. *IUCN Publs N.S.* **7**, 218-223.
WESTHOFF, V., OTTO, H. and BAKKER, P. A. (1968). Standplaatsen van *Corrigiola litoralis* L. *Gorteria* **4**, 137-145.
WiiNSTEDT, K. (1935). *Corrigiola littoralis* L. *Bot. Tidsskr.* **43**, 235-236.
WiiNSTEDT, K. (1940). Danske jernbaneplanter. *Bot. Tidsskr.* **45**, 195-199.
WRIGHT, I. C. (1963). Railways and wild life. *Rly. Mag.* **109**, 726-730.

DISCUSSION

Mr M. G. SCHULTZ asked whether the abandonment of railways in East Anglia had caused the loss of species locally.

Mr LOUSLEY replied that it had not yet. But as old railway lines were taken into adjoining farms or became overgrown with scrub, losses would occur.

Dr K. MELLANBY pointed out how much natural regeneration of oak wood occurs on railway embankments on a great variety of soil: absence of grazing is an important factor.

Mr C. J. CADBURY asked whether the use of salt on roads was creating a new halophyte habitat.

Mr A. J. GRAY commented that Dr. D. Ranwell of the Nature Conservancy had carried out tests on the verges of trunk roads and found salt concentrations equal to those occurring in the middle-level of saltmarshes.

THE MANAGEMENT AND PLANTING OF MOTORWAY VERGES

A. P. Dunball

Horticultural Adviser, Ministry of Transport

The impact of motorways on the landscape

Botanists may well be rather worried by the Ministry of Transport's expanding road building programme and the way in which new roads destroy so much of the natural landscape.

There was little concern when the first section of the M1 was driven through Herts, Beds, Bucks, and Northants, but when the M50 Ross Spur was built through some delightful unspoilt country where wild daffodils grow, I am sure a few pulses began to quicken. At present the M6 is being extended up the Lune Valley through Westmorland and on to Carlisle. The gap in the M4 will soon be closed and the motorway will cross some fine downland country. Eventually the M5 will be extended well down into Somerset.

A motorway is a very permanent structure and those being built today will no doubt outlast all other contemporary building. Housing and industrial development and, perhaps even nuclear power stations, will be torn down and the sites redeveloped, but the roads we are building today will remain. They will be improved and reconstructed over the years, but land lost to roads is lost for good.

A motorway is an unyielding structure the standards of which cannot be varied to suit the type of country through which it passes. Unfortunately they have to be designed primarily to meet the needs of traffic rather than the demands of the landscape. Bends must not be less than a given radius and gradients have to be gentle. Consequently in undulating country frequent cuttings and embankments have to be formed and small hills have to be dissected rather than by-passed. This may often appear brutal in areas of intimate, small scale, countryside.

To see a motorway under construction can be a disturbing experience. During site clearance a swaithe of countryside 200 ft or so wide, 25 acres to the mile, is completely devastated, and all plant and animal communities relentlessly obliterated. The vast earthmoving equipment then comes on to the site and the formation of the cuttings and embankments commences in seas of mud, or clouds of dust, depending on the season, completely ruining any peace and quiet the area ever possessed.

When the road building is over things do not return to normal, there is then the noise of the traffic and the movement of pleasure-bound motorists that the improved communications bring. It is worth bearing in mind that soon the Lake District will be only 2½ hours from the Midland conurbation and Dartmoor will be only 3½ hours from London. The town dweller will have far easier access to the countryside and areas such as these are bound to be used for recreation by far more people than at present. It is not only the physical effect of roads on the countryside which is important, but also the effect of their use by an increasing number of visitors.

The potential for natural plant communities

This is the 'Changing Britain' as far as road building is concerned and on the surface it seems a pretty black picture. However, as far as the flora is concerned, there is another side to the coin and that is really what I wish to write about here. Although we lose a great deal through road construction we gain a great potential and, although at present the credits may not balance the debits, I hope in time they will more than do so.

I mentioned just now that motorways take 25 acres of land per mile, this was a generalisation. The minimum width of land required to accommodate the road surface, the hardshoulders, the central reserve and verges is 112 ft, which gives a land take of 13·6 acres a mile. However, unless the road is running on level ground further land is required for the formation of cutting and embankment slopes, and the amount of land needed will vary according to the depth of the cutting or the height of the embankment. Further land is needed for junctions—and the large ones such as the M4/M5 junction at Almondsbury take over 100 acres—so that the figure I quoted can be taken as an approximate average. An interesting point is that the actual hard surfaced areas are only 93 ft wide taking 11·3 acres a mile, so assuming the average land take is 25 acres there are 13·7 acres of grass for every mile of motorway. This will give us 13,700 when the 1,000 mile target is reached and more will follow.

This land is completely sterilized for any commercial use and has no pedestrian access. Forming a pattern covering the four corners of our country the motorway system will eventually cross most soil types and climatic conditions. As Moore (1967) has pointed out this provides us with a tremendous potential for the development of our flora and if all road verges are taken into account they cover an area which is of the same order and magnitude as the National Nature Reserves. Although valuable agricultural land is lost to motorways the stock of marginal land, which is of much greater interest to the botanist, increases.

What the Ministry of Transport has had to decide is how to make the most of this potential to encourage the development of a rich and varied flora. In this the Minister has had the assistance of his Landscape Advisory Committee. This Committee, originally set up under the chairmanship of the Hon. Sir David Bowes-Lyon in 1956, advises the Minister on all amenity matters connected with road development and has amongst its members some of the leading landscape architects, horticulturalists and forestry experts in the country. Its present chairman is Sir George Taylor and although members represent such bodies as the Council for the Protection of Rural England, the motoring organisations, the Institute of Landscape Architects and the Royal Forestry Society others are completely independent and have been invited by the Minister to join the Committee in view of their specialised knowledge. Also the Ministry has established a close contact with the officers at the Nature Conservancy's Monks Wood Experimental Station, and is extremely grateful for the help and advice that has been received from them.

The design of planting schemes

During road construction natural growing conditions are radically changed. The topsoil is stripped from the site and stored in large stacks for 18 months or so. During this period the soil, especially that which is most deeply buried, deteriorates through lack of air and moisture and many of the micro-organisms which go to make topsoil a viable material disappear. Following the removal of the topsoil the cuttings and embankments are constructed to create a road of acceptable gradients. Normally the schemes are designed so that the material excavated from the cuttings is sufficient to form the embankments.

This creates another problem in that embankments may be formed of material quite foreign to the area. A chalk embankment may be built on acid heathland or where fill material is short industrial waste material such as shale or fly-ash may be imported. The pH of the topsoil itself may vary considerably over the length of a contract and acid soil may be spread in an alkaline area and vice versa.

Both the topsoil and the subsoil suffer great physical damage during the engineering works. The latter has to be compacted to support the road and avoid any later subsidence, and the former is also compressed by the earthmoving equipment which spreads it over the site. The finished growing medium is a 4-8 in. layer of an inert form of topsoil over a heavily compacted base. There is no natural drainage through the soil and it lies waterlogged in the winter and becomes hard and baked during the summer.

As a step towards the rehabilitation of motorway marginal-land planting schemes are prepared. The principle which governs the design of these schemes is now quite clear and fairly well known. Briefly, the main objects of the planting are the restoration of the landscape, the softening of the line of the motorway and the form of the earthworks, and the screening of unsightly views. A variation between planted and unplanted areas, openness and enclosure, can make a motorway more interesting to travel along and help relieve boredom. Any planting has to be in scale with both the road and the speed of the traffic using it. On slow country lanes individual plants can be picked out in the hedgerows, and detail can be appreciated. On fast roads it is only the general disposition of trees and shrubs which make any impact, and planting must be on a large scale to avoid being a fussy irritation.

In rural areas all planting must appear as natural as possible and the pattern formed by tree groups, individual trees and hedges must be repeated within the motorway boundary. Groups of trees which immediately adjoin the road may be extended within its boundary, the severed ends of hedges must be restored and hedgerow trees must be replaced. When new roads cross treeless heaths and moors obviously any planting would be out of place and would only emphasise the artificiality of the highway.

The problems of plant establishment

Following this line of thinking logically the species selected for use in the planting schemes should be the same as those growing in the immediate vicinity, and it is on this basis that schemes are prepared. However, in practice it is impossible to follow this principle strictly. As I have just mentioned there is a considerable mixing of soil types and this alone prevents the duplication of the species which adjoin the motorway boundary. Even more restricted are the general poor soil conditions and the exposed nature of the sites which are usually only suitable to hardy pioneer species. For this reason it is seldom possible to establish climax species such as oak and beech and the trees most commonly used are sycamore, ash, birch, grey alder, *Alnus incana*, and willow. Often conifers have to be planted, although foreign to the area, in order to provide shelter and protection for more desirable species.

Various measures have been tried to overcome these practical problems, the majority designed to improve the physical structure of the soil without affecting the stability of the earthworks. Most of the planting is done on 1:2 slopes which severely limits the type of equipment that can be employed. At present hand held motorised augers are used to prepare holes and to fracture the consolidated material. The excavated soil may be improved by the addition of peat and spent hops and returned to the hole, or it may be discarded altogether and fresh soil imported. Once the planted trees are established fertilizers are used to stimulate growth and encourage deep root penetration.

Experience over the last eight years has shown that the small 2 year old tree is much easier to establish and quicker to grow than the 6-8 ft horticultural standard. In fact at a site on the M6 trees 18-24 in. high were planted in 1963 in a forestry plot alongside 6-8 ft specimens. There is now no difference in height between the 2 plantings and the annual extension growth of the trees in the forestry plot is far greater than that of the standards. Small forestry transplants create no immediate visual effect but give more rapid results than larger material.

Within the limitations I have mentioned all new motorways are planted with indigenous trees and shrubs after construction. The planting plans are prepared by the Ministry of Transport's horticultural staff in consultation with local planning authorities, the

Ministry's planting agent, and the engineers responsible for the motorway. Once the plans have been approved by the Minister's Landscape Advisory Committee they are passed to the Ministry's planting agents who plant and maintain the schemes under the direction of the Ministry's horticultural staff. In all but 8 counties in England and Wales the Forestry Commission acts as the Ministry's planting agent, and in these 8 the County Authority has adequate qualified staff and an organisation capable of carrying out the work.

In the main I have referred to tree planting, but large numbers of shrubs are used annually. Hawthorn, hazel, blackthorn, goat willow, elder, dogwood and other indigenous species are planted in large quantities. To give you some idea of the amount of planting undertaken by the Ministry of Transport, during the last season 330,498 shrubs and 486,889 trees were used on trunk roads and motorways making a total of 817,387. However, using mainly small plants as I have mentioned, the cost of this work is not high The amount of planting which is necessary in any mile of motorway will vary tremendously, but the average cost of the work is £1,500-£2,000 a mile; this represents about 0·25% of the cost of motorway construction. For this sum we get planting on a very large scale, and amenity planting schemes comparable in size with that being carried out on the 195 miles of the M1 have not been attempted in this country since the height of the 18th century landscape movement.

Maintenance of banks and verges

The completion of the planting of a new motorway is by no means the completion of the landscape schemes. It lays down the foundation for the formation of hedges, scrub areas, small copses and spinneys, and groups of individual trees, but regular maintenance is essential to ensure that the initial planting thrives and produces the desired effect. This will produce communities of woody plants but the herbage between has still to be considered.

It has been suggested that new roads should be sown with more varied herbage mixtures, and that less grass and more indigenous dicotyledons should be used. However, there are difficulties in this, apart from the acquisition of the seed. The grass serves a practical purpose of binding the banks, increasing their stabilization, and preventing the surface erosion of topsoil. It is therefore necessary to get a good ground cover as soon as possible and the sowing of a grass-seed mixture is the best way of achieving this. Regular mowing is necessary for the first 2 or 3 years in order to get a dense sward and to eliminate such noxious weeds as docks and thistles (Weeds Act 1959). If the seeds of desirable herbs were included in the original mixture many would be eliminated along with the injurious weeds. Again, suiting the herbaceous species to the soil conditions over the length of a scheme would involve the use of several different seed mixtures and thus make the operation rather complicated.

Although grass is the initial cover there is no reason why

maintenance should be aimed at keeping a pure turf.   Once true weeds have been removed mowing frequencies can be reduced to encourage the naturalisation of a wide range of plants.

Way (1969b) has laid down a series of trials to ascertain the effect of various maintenance regimes on roadside flora.   Some of these are being carried out on the M1 and should indicate the type of maintenance which will support the most diverse flora.

The Ministry of Transport has given instructions to its maintaining authorities which set out variations in the standard of grass maintenance; these range from the central reserves which should be closely mown, to embankment slopes in woodland areas which should, after the initial establishment period, be left uncut.   The Ministry also exerts a strict control over the use of selective weed-killers, grass growth inhibitors and other chemicals.

The result of this, even if not necessarily the prime object, is to provide habitats for a wide range of plants.   Taking the planted areas into account motorways, and also the newer trunk roads, will be able to support species of woodland, scrub, rough grassland and pasture on a wide range of soils under differing climatic conditions. Colonisation is not fast, but the observant botanist will already have spotted the more showy species such as primrose, cowslip, wood anemone, soapwort and bluebells on the old section of the M1 and no doubt a botanical analysis between St. Albans and Crick would reveal a wide selection of the species commonly found on road verges.

REFERENCES

MOORE, N. W. (1967).   Nature Conservation.   In Williams, Ellis C. (1967).

PERRING, F. H. (1969).   The botanical importance of roadside verges.   In Way, J. M. (1969a).   8-14.

WAY, J. M. (Ed.) (1969a).   *Road Verges. Their Function and Management* Nature Conservancy.   Monks Wood Experimental Station.

WAY, J. M. (1969b).   Road verges—research on management for amenity and wildlife.   In Way, J. M. (1969a).   61-71.

WILLIAMS, Ellis C. (Ed.) (1967).   *Roads in the Landscape.*   H.M.S.O., London.

DISCUSSION

Mr R. M. BURTON asked the origin of the grass-seed mixtures sown.

Mr DUNBALL said that the majority came from this country: most mixture contained S.23, perennial rye-grass, S.59, creeping red fescue, *Poa pratensis*, *Cynosurus cristatus* and S.100, white clover.

Mr P. S. GREEN asked the origin of the trees which are planted.

Mr DUNBALL said that the majority were bought from the horticultural trade: *Crataegus monogyna* was imported from the Continent either as seed or seedlings.

SEED DISPERSAL BY BIRDS

M. E. GILLHAM

*University College of South Wales and
Monmouthshire, Cardiff*

Introduction

Had the subject of this symposium concerned "The Changing distribution of the British Flora" on a world scale rather than on a domestic scale, far more impressive data could have been assembled to illustrate the role played by birds. As far away as Australia and New Zealand—and to the chagrin of local botanists—colonially nesting birds are killing out patches of the indigenous flora and planting noxious British aliens in their stead. A tour of gull colonies can, in fact, be a tour of the oases of British weed species which are insinuating themselves irrevocably around the temperate coasts of both Southern and Northern Hemispheres. Their particular success in the Antipodes is probably related to the scarcity of easily dispersed annual ruderals in the native flora. Examples include patches of *Hordeum* in a West Australian silver-gull colony and of *Urtica* in a South African colony of mixed gulls and cormorants.

Similar changes are occurring within the bounds of Britain, but are less spectacular because they involve merely a re-shuffling of plants already abundant, instead of their dissemination from small localised points of introduction.

Factors necessary to successful transport

Like any other story, seed transport by birds can be divided into three parts, the beginning, the middle and the end.

1. *Source of supply.* This must be considered in relation to the birds' feeding and preening habits. If birds do not come to eat in the rickyard where the seeds are scattered or to preen on the muddy shores where they have been washed up, this method of dispersal is void.

2. *Duration of attachment.* The duration of attachment of the plant disseminules to the individual offering transport is of obvious significance. Externally there is a high possibility of their being shed during the normal movements of flight. Internally there is a high possibility of their being destroyed in the normal course of digestion, or defaecated before a suitable receiving area is reached.

Where birds are swimming rather than flying the hazards are increased. Non-maritime seeds carried externally may be killed by sea salt and those carried internally have more chance of being prematurely ejected, either forwards as a crop pellet or backwards as a faecal pellet, because of the slower mode of progression. Harrison (1931) showed that small food leftovers can get lodged in folds of the walls of an apparently empty digestive system and such 'forgotten fragments' could conceivably remain within the bird for very much longer than the average stomach contents. Insect remains which he had identified from within a honey buzzard had been transported from SW France to Kent!

A very relevant observation by de Vlaming and Proctor (1968) is that propagules of water plants may remain in a mallard's stomach up to at least 70 hours. In direct flight, with a following wind, this opens up the possibility of transport over considerable distance—even to the involvement of 'Amphi-Atlantics'.

3. *Suitability of receiving habitat.* Introduced into a densely vegetated area, newcomers will probably fail to establish themselves or even to make contact with the soil. If the indigenous vegetation is kept short by grazing, as where crop pellets are deposited on the close *Hydrocotyle-Littorella* sward of seasonally flooded clifftop they have a better chance. Patches of arable weeds whose seeds have been identified in the crop pellets of gulls are common in the open cliff feeding grounds of herring gulls but are seldom seen in the bracken and grass communities occupied by lesser black-backed gulls.

Ridley (1930) cites an example of a shearwater being found at sea with a large number of seeds attached to its plumage and argues that this proves mass transport. Factors not taken into account were first that shearwaters spend long periods at sea—the entire non-breeding season—and secondly that they come ashore only at the nesting islands, alighting as near their burrows as possible, so that any plant disseminules surviving the long dowsing in salt water are likely to return to the spot from whence they came. The Procellariiformes, or 'tube-nosed' petrel group, do not normally have the opportunity to introduce seeds, but they play an important role in preparing a suitable habitat for chance arrivals, by clearing space and depositing nutrients. This can be seen by the localisation of lush *Stellaria media* around nesting fulmars on the cliffs of Fair Isle.

External transport

Botanists finding strange plants in strange places and gardeners rooting out cotoneasters from their gravel paths, are apt automatically to attribute the vagrants to bird carriage. Ornithologists who handle many birds in the course of ringing, state flatly that birds healthy enough to undertake flights of any length preen away all foreign bodies (apart from their normal complement of ectoparasites) before taking off. The truth, no doubt, lies somewhere between the two.

1. *Bur fruits.* The text books tell us that bur fruits are made that way for clutching on to mammals, birds and socks for transport to new areas. Few texts suggest that they might be made for clinging to new areas when they arrive by other means. *Zostera,*

Ceratophyllum and *Zannichellia* are genera intimately associated with foraging wildfowl, but are more likely to rely on water transport than bird transport for their dispersal, the hooks on their drifting fruits serving to anchor them in shifting mud on arrival at a new site.

Waterfowl may help with water transport by rooting out plant fragments in the course of their search for food, these floating away to form new colonies. This may be achieved by carnivores seeking small molluscs and crustaceans or by herbivores 'biting off more than they can chew'. Mute swans and certain geese are particularly wasteful feeders, plant fragments drifting in large quantities onto shores where they have been feeding.

Fruits which are viscid as well as hooked cling like spiders' webs and it is not uncommon to find small birds completely incapacitated by these under *Pisonia* trees in the Tropics. Larger birds such as terns and noddies might transport these to other islands, but no British examples spring immediately to mind.

2. *Small seeds adhering in mud.* Small seeds adhering to the feet of water birds are, perhaps, better fitted to escape being preened off. Monocoyledonous seeds are particularly prone to this method, common examples being *Alisma, Juncus, Carex, Cyperus* and *Glyceria*. Many rush seeds, like those of plantains and *Littorella*, are mucilagenous when moistened and could adhere in their own right without mud. The added weight of mud is more likely to get preened off to give buoyancy for flight than are seeds alone. Certainly these put in unheralded appearances around isolated ponds and various workers have tried to correlate these appearances with the major flyways of migratory birds, which may deviate considerable distances to visit bodies of water sighted from the flight path.

During the course of the peculiar stimulatory activity known as 'anting', some birds, particularly members of the Corvidae, sift the fine soil of anthills through their feathers and may get small seeds lodged among the plumage in the process. The same might be suggested for the familiar dust bathing of house sparrows etc., but this seems unlikely as this activity is part of a preening routine to get rid of foreign bodies rather than acquire them.

3. *Nest material.* This is usually gathered locally, so accounts for little dispersal, but it may be important in initiating the colonisation of new habitats by plants. An obvious example is of gulls nesting on bare rock, shingle or sand. These birds bring in quantities of vegetable material, only part of which is likely to be viable, but all adds organic matter to the sterile substrate, making growth of the viable part, or of later arrivals, possible.

Colonially nesting gulls are associated with an early phase of the plant succession consisting principally of annuals. Usually they degrade a more advanced succession back to this phase—as in the first example (p. 90) where the annual *Hordeum* was replacing the perennial *Carpobrotus*. On sterile substrata they serve to advance the succession to a higher phase by bringing in plants where none grew before. A plant commonly established in this way is *Bromus sterilis*, which is by no means sterile, producing abundant scabrid, awned fruits likely to be dispersed by animals in the normal course of events.

4. *Food for storage.* This is collected and cached, not only by squirrels, but by birds, particularly members of the crow family. The same result is achieved when acorns, beechmast and the like are dropped by pigeons. Jays bury quantities of acorns, failing to return for many of them, and are often given the credit for dispersing oakwoods uphill, the seeds being too cumbrous to go by other means. Schuster (1950) recorded an average of 4,600 acorns transported per individual jay in a single season, some of these being taken to a forest 4 km away. Although the average is less, extremes obviously count in this context.

As with wind transport, allowance must be made for wastage, but the regularity of bird transport makes this an acceptable method for oaks, and also often for hazels. Limitations are imposed by the fact that jays are unlikely to bury nuts in open heathland and initiate a new forest. Usually they employ woodland sites, planting trees where more may not be needed to maintain the forest. They may well play a part, however, in speeding the natural succession from wind-dispersed, light-demanding birch to less easily dispersed, shade-tolerant oak and thus changing the face of the countryside qualitatively.

Rooks have been observed burying acorns and hazel nuts, and these are more likely to plant them in the open than are jays. Woodpeckers and nuthatches often wedge nuts in crevices of trees to be hammered open and eaten. Nuts abandoned in sites of high atmospheric humidity may germinate as epiphytes, but the presence of a few precariously perched nut trees is unlikely to make a significant difference to the conformation of the forest. Effectual colonisation is more likely to be secondary here, and dependent upon the nuts being removed to ground level by rodents.

It is interesting to note in this connection that the horse chestnut, *Aesculus*, which is more than a mouthful for the average seed eating bird, was unable to follow the retreating ice back to northern Britain as the oak and hazel did.

Internal transport

1. *Seed-eating birds.* These birds have a digestive system capable of breaking down seeds; otherwise life would prove unprofitable for them. Some, like finches, shell the seed in the beak before swallowing it. Fermentation occurs in the crop, grinding in the gizzard, with the help of stones swallowed for the purpose, and absorption in the intestine, which is longer than in birds of prey. Hess (1951) states that steel needles can be bent between the horny-ridged grinding surfaces of the gizzard of a seed eater without perforating the gizzard wall!

In spite of this, Kempski (1969) found that 4% of the seeds

eaten by pigeons and hens were voided intact and 25% of these germinated. More may survive in the droppings of wood pigeons, crows, starlings, sparrows and pheasants, and the sojourn in the birds' gut can prove beneficial to seeds. Not only may slight digestion of the resistant testa facilitate the entry of water and exit of plumule and radicle during germination, but the dung in which the seed is 'planted' could have both a corrosive and a nutritive influence. Just as certain woody *Eucalyptus* capsules have become adapted during evolution to germinate only after forest fires (when replacement trees are most needed), so small, hard seeds may have become adapted to germinating only after internal carriage to new sites.

Ducks swallow enormous numbers of seeds during the course of their foraging and may deposit these, unharmed, at a considerable distance if migrating. Because they usually come down in the same, watery, type of habitat, they can be fairly sure of leaving these in a suitable environment: Sedges (Cyperaceae), water lilies, both *Nuphar* and *Nymphaea*, pondweeds, *Potamogeton,* and arrowhead, *Sagittaria* are important in this connection, and seeds of *Potamogeton* have been found to germinate only after passage through a bird, or after such passage has been simulated experimentally. Olney (1963, 1965, 1967) in a series of publications on the feeding habits of waterfowl, has included the following species as supplying seeds for foraging duck.

Ranunculus aquatilis agg.	P. pusillus
R. repens	P. pectinatus
Ceratophyllum demersum	P. gramineus
Medicago lupulina	P. coloratus
Crataegus monogyna	P. filiformis
Rubus fruticosus agg.	P. obtusifolius
Rosa spp.	Sparganium erectum
Myriophyllum sp.	S. emersum
Hippuris vulgaris	S. angustifolium
Rumex conglomeratus	Ruppia sp.
Polygonum amphibium	Juncus inflexus
P. persicaria	Juncus spp.
P. hydropiper	Eleocharis palustris
P. lapathifolium	Scirpus lacustris
P. nodosum	S. maritimus
Atriplex patula	Carex hirta
Chenopodium album	Carex spp.
Suaeda maritima	Holcus lanatus
Salicornia spp.	Phleum pratense
Alnus glutinosa	Glyceria fluitans
Quercus robur	G. declinata
Betula spp.	Bromus sterilis
Armeria maritima	Phalaris arundinacea
Galium aparine	Alopecurus geniculatus
Sambucus nigra	Lolium multiflorum
Taraxacum palustre	Poa trivialis
Cirsium palustre	Phragmites communis
Potamogeton natans	Triticum aestivum
P. perfoliatus	Hordeum distichon
P. berchtoldii	

Sometimes it is difficult to envisage other means of transport, a case in point being the rare and handsome South American sedge, *Cyperus eragrostis*, which turned up at the new Guernsey Reservoir around 1961 and then in 1968 at the Jersey Reservoir, some thirty miles distant, only two years after this was constructed. The two possibilities here seem to be seed-eating finches during the dry phase or dabbling ducks after autumn flooding and possible seed shedding.

Seeds ingested by birds do not always pass right through, but may be ejected as a crop pellet. Pellets thrown up by gulls feeding on cereal grains can be found at any time of the year. Sometimes these consist of chaff and crushed seed remains only, but quite often of almost undamaged grains. 119 apparently viable oat grains taken from a single pellet on the Skokholm cliffs showed a 64% germination by the ninth day when planted in ordinary garden soil.

As gulls have individual feeding preferences and individual standing and preening grounds, fair-sized colonies of oats, wheat and barley may spring up in their clifftop haunts—even as far out to sea as Grassholm Island, which is 11 or 12 miles from the nearest cornfield or rickyard.

2. *Fruit-eating birds.* These inevitably take in seeds during the course of their foraging, but are seldom capable of digesting them. Being visual feeders, with little or no sense of smell, they tend to go for bright colours, particularly red, as do nectar-feeding bird pollinators (which must also be given some credit for the success of seed production and establishment). Contrasting colours, as supplied by the arils of yew, *Taxus,* and spindle, *Euonymus,* have a special attraction.

Seeds may get no further than the beak, in which case transport is very local. An obvious example is mistletoe, *Viscum album,* after which the mistle thrush, *Turdus viscivorus* is named in both the vernacular and the scientific. The bird is irritated by the viscid, clinging nature of the seeds and wipes them off the beak in a crevice, where their viscosity serves to anchor them until a haustorial root can be sent into the host. Honeysuckle, *Lonicera,* is another shrub with sticky fruits.

Pip spitting by thrushes, blackbirds, robins, starlings and the like is commonly observed, sometimes a single large pip as of ivy, *Hedera,* or hawthorn, *Crataegus,* which consists mostly of stone, sometimes a pea-sized ball of smaller ones, sometimes a well-formed oval crop pellet. The deposition of pips (which can be readily collected from bird tables and beneath favourite perches for identification) is invariably preceded by a series of gulping motions, indicating that the pips have got at least as far as the crop before being brought back, and have hence had the opportunity of travelling from their point of intake. Blackbirds may eject four or five small crop pellets in rapid succession, separated only by fast, repeated retching. Single pellets ejected by this species may measure 1×0.25 in. (24×6 mm).

Regurgitation is sometimes from the gizzard rather than the crop, with greater possibility of mechanical and chemical softening of the hard seed coat, and implying a longer travelling time.

Frequently seeds pass right through the alimentary canal and the purple, seed-studded droppings of autumn are a familiar sight. 24 different species of passerines were listed in *British Birds* (1962) as feeding on blackberries at Dungeness, and the noxious spread of British brambles, *Rubus fruticosus* agg., in Australia and New Zealand is attributed initially to birds, boosted by subsequent rooting of arching stems.

Hess (1951) states that berries remain in a thrush's stomach for 45 minutes on average, but that pips may be evacuated in as little as 12 minutes after swallowing.   This time of retention is of vital importance in the colonisation of new islands and involves the study of facilitating agents such as the speed of following winds hastening the passage of vagrants and migrants (see pp. 90-91).

Another climatic factor affecting seed dispersal is temperature. In a cold spring, when insect larvae are in short supply, nestlings may be fed almost exclusively on the late-maturing ivy fruits and nests become lined with a thick layer of ivy seeds.   Wood pigeons eat these fruits well into May and little colonies of ivy seedlings spring up abundantly in gardens which they frequent.

In mild winters the less palatable fruits are left until last and may not be eaten at all—the orange berries of sea buckthorn, *Hippophae rhamnoides,* remaining on the bushes, bleached but intact, well into April.   Those with irritant hairs may be taken selectively; the hips of *Rosa arvensis* may be pecked whilst those of *Rosa canina* are left alone.   In very open winters, such plants must rely on wind dispersal of seeds after the fruits have withered.

Tropical forest birds can subsist entirely on fruits.   British fruits occur only seasonally and the fruit-eaters, being necessarily more omnivorous, may spurn fruits when they are available.   (It is always pleasant to see blackbirds eating earthworms in preference to raspberries).   Tits feeding on yew are more likely to be breaking open the seeds with their all-purpose bills than eating the flesh, and they will open up seeds discarded by thrushes thus annulling the good work performed by their fellow foragers.

3. *Grazing birds.* Swans and geese digest crude fibre less efficiently than do mammals (Ranwell and Downing 1959), relying more on crushing in the gizzard than on enzyme action for the breakdown of cellulose.   It is interesting in this connection that island sheep and cattle in the Hebrides and Western Ireland derive considerable nourishment by eating the droppings of barnacle and other geese before the 'early bite' appears in the spring pastures. Leafy stem fragments an inch or two long can be extracted, apparently undamaged, from swan or goose dung and such fragments of water plants are quite large enough to put out adventitious roots and multiply.

4. *Omnivorous birds.* Birds such as gulls, are very likely to pick up weed seeds in the course of foraging for other material, usually of animal origin.   This is undoubtedly the principle way in which new species reach our island gulleries, although van der

Pijl (1969) discounts indiscriminate picking up of seeds as no more than 'a theoretical possibility'.

Pellets ejected by such birds are either neatly egg-shaped packs of beetle carapaces, caterpillar skins or crab, bird or rabbit remains, or are less regular and of fibrous plant material. Almost 100 seeds, most of them viable, have been extracted from a single pellet found in a Welsh island roost, but 10-20 is a more usual number. Seldom are there none at all. Species identified include:

Stellaria media	*Rumex spp.*
Cerastium sp.	*Plantago lanceolata*
Spergula arvensis	*Anagallis arvensis*
Geranium molle	*Myosotis sp.*
Trifolium sp.	*Cynosurus cristatus*
Polygonum persicaria	*Festuca sp.*
P. aviculare agg.	*Poa annua*

Further ruderals growing conspicuously among island accumulations of pellets for a single season but failing to persist are *Sinapis arvensis, Brassica oleracea, Kickxia elatine* and *Picris hieracioides*. Others, more persistent, are *Arabis hirsuta, Coronopus didymus, Capsella bursa-pastoris, Plantago major, Senecio vulgaris, Chrysanthemum segetum* and *Matricaria matricarioides*.

A small fruiting tomato plant, *Lycopersicum,* was found in August 1969 on one of the bird stacks off Guernsey, many of the gull pellets on a nearby islet consisting of screwed up tomato skins with a sprinkling of viable pips. The Guernseyman's maincop of so-called 'chemical ping-pong balls' needs a high nutrient level in the soil, and that in the soil of bird colonies is eminently suitable, even when photosynthesis is curtailed by surface deposits of guano.

Rubbish-tip scavenging is the normal mode of feeding for thousands of gulls in our modern urban community and exotic weed seeds as well as native ones can turn up among the expectorated candle ends, plum stones, bottle-tops, coke and neatly rolled paper bags. The trampled wasteland on which they are deposited bears a fair resemblance to that of the tips—except aesthetically— and conditions are usually right for germination, if not for permanent establishment.

Over the course of millions of years, plant disseminules may need to arrive only once to become part of the flora. With the odds against successful passage at a million to one, it would still be more surprising that they had not achieved this than that they had.

REFERENCES

DE VLAMING, V. and PROCTOR, V. (1968). Dispersal of aquatic angiosperms. *Am. J. Bot.* **55**, 20.

GILLHAM, M. E. (1956a). Ecology of the Pembrokeshire Islands. V. Manuring and seed distribution by birds. *J. Ecol.* **44**, 429-454.

GILLHAM, M. E. (1956b). Feeding habits of mute swans on two S. Devon estuaries. *Bird Study* **3**, 205-212.

GILLHAM, M. E. (1967). Ejection of crop pellets by small passerines. *Int. Bird Pellet Study Grp. Bull.* **2**, 2.

HARRISON, J. (1931). Stomach contents of honey buzzard shot in Kent. *Ibis*
13, 772-773.

HESS, G. (1951). *The Bird, its Life and Structure*. Berlin.

OLNEY, P. J. S. (1963). Food and feeding habits of tufted duck. *Ibis* 105,
56-62.

OLNEY, P. J. S. (1967). Feeding ecology of local mallard and other wildfowl.
Wildfowl Trust. 18th Ann. Rep. 47-55.

PIJL, L. VAN DER. (1969). *Principles of Dispersal in Higher Plants*. New York.

RANWELL, D. S. and DOWNING, B. M. (1959). Brent goose winter feeding
pattern and *Zostera* resources at Scolt Head I., Norfolk. *Anim. Behav.*
7, 42-56.

RIDLEY, H. N. (1930). *The Dispersal of Plants throughout the World*. Ashford.

SCHUSTER, L. (1950). Über den sammeltrieb des Eichelhähers *(Garrulus)*.
Vogelwelt 71, 9-17.

SPENCER, R. (1962). [British-ringed manx shearwater recovered in Australia]
Br. Birds 55, 87-88.

DISCUSSION

Mr LOUSLEY said that the fig was one of the most obvious examples of a
species which must be spread by birds to places like church towers. In the
Isles of Scilly *Carpobrotus* was clearly spread by gulls to uninhabited islands.

Dr GILLHAM said *Carpobrotus* was used in S. Africa as the main nesting
material of penguins.

OUR FILTHY WORLD—THE POLLUTION OF LAND AIR AND WATER

K. MELLANBY

Nature Conservancy,
Monks Wood Experimental Station, Huntingdon

Introduction

My task is to introduce discussion of the effects of chemicals on the flora of Britain. The two following papers deal specifically with the effects of herbicides on arable weeds, and with the ways poisons in the air affect plants, so I will not deal with these problems in any detail.

The increase in population, the spread of our towns, and the intensity of our industrial development, are all factors which may increase the filthiness of Britain. Dumps and spoil heaps from mines and smelting works have affected large areas, and have generally exterminated the more interesting elements in the flora in the vicinity. At times rubbish dumps have enriched our flora by introducing exotic species of plants, a development not always welcomed by conservationists. The selection of strains of grasses able to withstand high concentrations of toxic metals like zinc and copper on industrial tips is an interesting side-effect of pollution, and one whose importance may have been underestimated. Population increase, the spread of urban sprawl and increased industrialisation not only increases pollution, it also increases the pressure on the remaining rural areas, with each deleterious factor reinforcing the effects of the others. Pollution on restricted 'natural areas' surrounded by industrial development, will be more intense than in a widespread rural area.

Previous papers have stressed the important effects of modern agriculture, and of other changes in land use. It is not always possible to separate effects of these developments from the effects of chemical pollution. In agriculture, for instance, pollution may arise in many different ways, from a variety of changes in cropping, fertilizer usage, animal husbandry and pest control, and the importance of the different factors may be hard to evaluate. These pollutions arising from agriculture may be very hard to control, and may have profound ecological effects.

Dr. Bowen, in his paper (p. 119), gives details of the amounts of the major air pollutants, smoke, sulphur dioxide and fluoride, which are emitted, and he discusses their effects on plants. There are clear cut effects on lichens, with important changes in the distribution of sensitive species particularly in urban areas and to the windward of our conurbations. Coniferous trees and some agricultural crops are sensitive, and instances of economic damage are not infrequent. However, there is little evidence of major changes in our wild flora from air pollution. There is probably more effect than is generally recognised, for differences in sensitivity must affect competition between different species, and the physiological effects of damage which cause no obvious morphological lesions is as difficult to study as the effects of sub-lethal amounts of insecticides on man and wildlife. I would consider this a fruitful field for future research.

Herbicides and insecticides

When modern herbicides came into general use after the last war, botanists saw a great risk to our flora. Mr. Fryer will show how the weeds in our arable crops have been affected. There have also been many incidents when herbicides have drifted from crops onto other vegetation, and done considerable damage. As a rule this damage has been transitory, with little long-term ecological effect. Herbicides have been washed off the land into rivers, doing serious damage to plant life; more about this will be said later. In general, however, the side effects on our flora have been comparatively slight. This is because most herbicides either break down quickly or, because of their chemical composition, they are not easily transferred from one area to another in the way the organochlorine insecticides are transmitted in food chains. Herbicides, used to kill one plant, do not usually become concentrated in some other plant which is not the target organism for the sprays. There are many herbicides which, wrongly used, could greatly affect our native flora. However, this seldom happens as a pollution problem. The danger of pesticides is that they may be so efficient, that they will make processes such as the ploughing and cultivation of marginal land possible. This marginal land often has some botanical importance, and this may be lost forever if the sward is ploughed either mechanically or chemically. Damage outside the area actually cultivated is usually minimal.

Insecticides are substances used to kill pest insects, and for the most part they have little direct effect on plants, though in high concentrations many have some phytotoxic properties. I do not think there is evidence of serious ecological effects from such phytotoxicity. The persistent organochlorine insecticides are well known to be transmitted in food chains and in other ways, and to have profound ecological effects on many animals, including raptorial birds and carnivorous mammals and on many species of insects also. Insecticidal pollution may have indirect botanical effects. Sprays may unintentionally kill bees and many of the wild insects which are important pollinators both of fruit trees and crops like clover and beans, and also of wild flowers. It is difficult to assess the relative importance of insecticides, and of the removal of habitats (e.g. hedge destruction) in this connection. The effects of the decrease in pollinating insects on economically-important plants are well known and have been widely studied, but little work on the effects on wild plants appears to have been done.   Does this change favour the spread of plants with efficient vegetative means of propagation? This seems another subject worthy of more study.

Water pollution

Pollution of land and air is a serious problem, with important ecological effects.   However, much more dramatic results are observed when water is polluted.   The aquatic fauna is obviously extremely susceptible to the effects of pollution.   Thus fish may be killed if put into water with a DDT level of 10^{-9}, though such water could be drunk safely by man for an indefinite period of time without significantly raising the level of pesticide in his tissues.   Aquatic plants are not, on the whole, quite as susceptible to pollution as are animals, though herbicides at very low levels can be effective.   Thus paraquat at a strength of half a part per million will kill most aquatic plants in lakes and reservoirs; sprays applied to terrestrial vegetation are only effective at much higher concentrations.   Accidental pollution by chemicals, such as cyanide, in industrial effluents, affects plants, but here again animal life is more seriously damaged by such accidents.   The most important effects of pollution of water on plants are probably the results of differential stimulation of certain species, rather than the actual killing of specific plants by toxic substances.

As has been said, the aquatic animals are very easily poisoned, and the aquatic fauna often affects the flora.   Gardeners know that they must have a healthy snail population in their ponds, to graze the algae and prevent them covering the water surface.   If the snails are killed, the algae pullulate.   Snails are not particularly easily eliminated by poisons, but crustacea appear to be very susceptible to organochlorine insecticides, and this can have dramatic effects.   One such case was demonstrated in 1968 in the Chew Valley Lake near Bristol.   This lake had been reasonably stable for some ten years, with no trouble from excessive algal growth, and trout flourished.   Then in the spring of 1968 an algal bloom occurred, producing conditions described as resembling pea soup, with a maximum count of unicellular plants of 610,000 per ml.   By a piece of brilliant detection, Mr. L. R. Bays of the Bristol Waterworks Company, showed that the ultimate cause was dieldrin pollution.   This had been used several years earlier as a sheep dip on a farm four miles distant from the lake, and had seeped underground eventually contaminating the lake.   Its effect had been to eliminate almost completely the minute crustacea which had been keeping the algae in check.

In the Chew Valley Lake, the water was rich enough in nutrients to allow the algae to bloom, but the crustacea were controlling this 'pest' biologically.   In many cases, in rivers, lakes and reservoirs, such control seldom occurs.   It is in fact the enrichment or eutrophication of our lowland waters which has the most serious biological effects, and which causes serious, and often irreversible, changes in the flora and fauna.

Eutrophication, the increase in the level of nutrient salts in waters, is a natural process. Most mountain streams and upland reservoirs are relatively pure with few salts. As the rivers run into the lowlands, water seeping through the adjacent soil increases the level of salts, and many lakes naturally reach high nutrient levels. This is all a gradual process, and though the effects on the fauna are profound, a comparatively stable situation usually exists. Man accelerates these changes enormously. First we have sewage effluents. Our watercourses have, since prehistoric days, been used as sewers. When populations were low, raw, untreated sewage did little biological damage. Parasites and diseases were no doubt transmitted, but the excrement broke down slowly and was, on the whole, beneficial to plant growth. With increased populations raw sewage had a very different effect, causing complete de-oxygenation and the virtual extermination of fish. Few plants other than some algae, fungi and bacteria survived. This sort of gross and stinking pollution is rare in Britain today, as less and less raw sewage is discharged into our rivers.

Britain has the highest standard of sewage treatment in the world, but sewage though clean and relatively safe (though some pathogens, particularly virus, may be found in most effluents) has profound biological effects. This is because the majority of the salts, particularly phosphates and nitrates, pass into the effluents. In fact the more efficient the processes of sewage disposal, the greater the amount of nutrient in the effluent. In areas in America where a high proportion of householders have their own garbage pulverising apparatus, the effects are even more spectacular.

Sewage effluent is a serious cause of eutrophication, particularly in rivers like the Thames and the Trent, which flow through populous areas. However, even greater amounts of nutrient salts reach our waters from agricultural sources. The use of chemical fertilisers is increasing greatly. The greater part of such fertiliser is not removed in the crop, but lost in other ways. There is no simple formula for use and loss, and some investigators have shown that the correlation between fertiliser application and nutrient levels in run-off is not a simple one, but in general the higher the fertiliser use the higher the nitrate levels in the waters. In America the results appear to be more clear-cut than in Britain.

The blame for eutrophication must be shared between sewage effluents and the run-off from agricultural land. In general, the greater part of the nitrate, in some cases as much as 80%, seems to come from farm land, but this water may be deficient in phosphate. In such cases we find high nitrate levels with little effect on the vegetation. High levels of phosphate are now found in sewage effluents, this being the results of the breakdown of synthetic detergents. The nuisance of detergent foam, which, while un-aesthetic had little harmful effect, and had the advantage of drawing attention to the state of some of our rivers, has been largely overcome by the development of 'soft' detergents which are broken down in the sewage plants, but the phosphate residues are still discharged. Plant growth may be affected by the interaction of nitrates from farms and phosphates from our washtubs.

Agriculture is adding to eutrophication in another way.   In the past the excrements of farm animals were used as manure, and maintained the fertility of the land.   Today this excrement is often an embarrassment to farmers.   With more and more animals kept indoors by farmers with little other land, and with systems where much wet slurry is produced, pollution is often the result.   Some slurry is passed into ordinary sewage plants, and this contributes to the level of salts in the effluent.   Some is, illegally, run into rivers without proper treatment, and this causes the effects previously experienced from the massive discharge of raw sewage.   Generally attempts are made to avoid this, and oxygenation ditches and other methods of disposal are used, but in most cases some of the matter, and particularly the nutrient salts, finds its way into the watercourses.

The effects of serious eutrophication in the flora may be devastating.   Commonly the whole surface is blanketed with filamentous algae, which prevents the light from penetrating the water, so no plants can survive below the blanket.   Then the algae die, and their decomposition even further reduces the oxygen level. All plants and animal life are affected.

Most eutrophication is not a symptom of our filthiness, but of our cleanliness.   As the population increases so our sewage effluent will be enriched.   Detergents may wash 'whiter than white', but their side-effects contribute substantially to the death of our rivers and lakes.

Conclusion

It is difficult to say just how important is the overall effect of pollution on our flora.   The effects in water are obviously catastrophic, but terrestrial plants are undoubtedly affected.   As already suggested, studies of lethal effects or even of severe morphological damage may be insufficient, and there may be much more subtle effects, altering the balance between competing species.   I am sure that the whole subject of the relations between different species of plants and environmental pollution is a fruitful one for intensified research.

DISCUSSION

Dr D. H. DALBY said that the damage to saltmarshes caused by a catastrophe releasing large quantities of oil over a short period was less great than the damage caused by the release of small quantities of oil over a long period.   Recovery from the former was rapid: the latter upsets the differential growth rate of salt-marsh plants and affects their competitive ability.

Dr MELLANBY commented that this was understandable as long as the catastrophe was not so great as to kill all the species so that recolonisation was impossible.

Mr T. CAVALIER-SMITH asked what were the possibilities of abstracting phosphate and nitrate from sewage to make fertilisers.

Dr MELLANBY replied that phosphate could be easily precipitated but nitrate could not. If water were fed into lagoons, algae might be grown in them which would take up the nitrate; they could then be harvested and used as food. It was more important to try to control what went into rivers than to abstract it after it had reached them.

Mr D. McCLINTOCK asked whether the use of herbicides was likely to result in resistant strains of plants developing.

Dr MELLANBY replied that it would depend what percentage of the species occurred within the habitat being sprayed. A weed almost exclusive to a particular type of crop might well develop resistant strains, if however only a small percentage of the population occurred in a crop any resistance built up there would be swamped by contact with the rest of the population.

Dr M. E. NEWTON said that because a plant had survived spraying, this did not mean it was not affected.

Dr MELLANBY agreed that some insecticides, for example, benzene hexa-chloride (BHC), act like colchicine, causing mutations.

Mrs F. LE SUEUR asked how she could get rid of a tin of surplus metasystox (an organo-phosphorus insecticide).

Dr MELLANBY replied that this was not a persistent insecticide. It should not be put down the drain but it could be disposed of in the normal way. In reply to a further question by Mr M. BROWN he said that 90% of pesticides used by gardeners were unnecessary. A little more untidyness would allow natural predators to exert biological control over our garden pests.

HERBICIDES AND OUR CHANGING WEEDS

J. D. FRYER and R. J. CHANCELLOR

Agricultural Research Council Weed Research Organisation,
Begbroke Hill, Yarnton, Oxford

Introduction

Plants only become known as weeds when they interfere with man's activities and interests. In his endeavours to cultivate crops, till the land or manage vegetation for his own ends, man modifies the environment and any plant that finds the new situation to its liking and multiplies may quickly become a weed. Conversely, a change in man's activities may interrupt the life cycle of a weed or produce an environment unfavourable to it and then it ceases to be one.

The effect of herbicides on the weed flora must therefore be viewed against changing agricultural practices, which in themselves have a profound effect upon the abundance and status of individual weed species. For example, corn-cockle, *Agrostemma githago*, virtually disappeared as a weed of arable land before the advent of herbicides because of improved methods of seed cleaning. Liming has probably been the main factor responsible for the diminishing importance of corn marigold, *Chrysanthemum segetum*, and perhaps of corn spurrey, *Spergula arvensis*. Many traditional annual weeds of arable land fail to germinate and grow on land that remains untilled. For this reason fruit growers practising non-cultivation systems of crop husbandry and farmers who have adopted direct-drilling of crops are finding that annual weeds diminish in importance, their place tending to be taken by biennials and perennials.

Whilst herbicides have been in use in cereal crops since the beginning of the century, the early ones were neither reliable nor very suitable. Chemicals were not widely used for weed control until after the commercial introduction of the synthetic plant growth regulators MCPA and 2,4-D in 1946. From that time there has been a steady flow of new chemicals from industry which have proved so valuable to farmers and growers that they have increasingly come to be regarded as essential tools in the production of agricultural and horticultural crops. They are seen as something much more than a simple substitute for the hoe. They are recognised to be unique tools of farm management. Through their ability to control one plant species growing amongst another by the simple act of spraying, which does not necessitate soil disturbance they have allowed the development of revolutionary new systems of crop production. Apart from being outstandingly efficient compared with many traditional forms of weed control, their use involves but little labour and machinery. For these and other reasons herbicides are being increasingly used in agriculture and horticulture throughout the world, and also for vegetation control on non-agricultural land and in waters.

In Britain, whilst no official statistics are available, it is likely that some two-thirds of the arable land is treated annually with herbicides. There are more than 300 proprietary products available to farmers and growers based on some 50 different chemicals. What effect has this great armoury of weedkilling weapons had on the weed flora in Britain so far? What information is available on this subject and what conclusions can be drawn from it regarding trends in the future? These are the questions we set ourselves and which we shall attempt to answer in this paper.

The information available to us can be grouped into three classes: general observations and opinions; weed surveys; and results of long-term experiments and scientific observations. In addition we are presenting some detailed assessments of the weed flora in two fields at the Weed Research Organization over 8 years to illustrate changes in weed populations. Because of the general paucity of information on the subject, we have included references to relevant papers from overseas.

General observations and opinions

Comments on the changes in the weed flora, that are thought to have taken place since the introduction of herbicides, occur from time to time in published articles. It is difficult to know how much importance to attach to many of these because it is seldom stated on what grounds the conclusions have been drawn.

Such observations have come from many parts of the world. In general there is a good measure of agreement in that they indicate that species that are markedly susceptible to herbicides, notably many dicotyledonous annuals, have declined, whereas resistant species, particularly grasses, have increased. A few examples are quoted below.

In Canada, Hay (1968) suggests that charlock, *Sinapis arvensis*, has decreased on the prairies, whilst some other broad-leaved weeds have increased, including cowcockle, *Saponaria vaccaria*, and tartary buckwheat, *Fagopyrum tartaricum*, also grass weeds, notably common wild-oat, *Avena fatua*.

In Australia (Dept. Agriculture, N.S.W. 1967) annual grasses such as *Avena* spp. and Wimmera ryegrass, *Lolium rigidum*, are reported as becoming a problem in winter cereals, possibly as a result of effective control of broad-leaved weeds.

In eastern U.S.A., the continuing and extensive use of atrazine in maize has resulted in increased infestations of crab-grasses, *Digitaria* spp., which are resistant (Peters 1967).

In Sweden, Aberg (1957) has suggested that the regular use of phenoxyacetic acid herbicides has apparently resulted in an increase in common couch, *Agropyron repens*, loose silky-bent, *Apera spica-venti, Avena fatua* and tolerant dicotyledons including scentless mayweed, *Tripleurospermum maritimum* and common cleavers, *Galium aparine*.

From the tropics information is sparse. In Trinidad it has been reported (Tate and Lyle 1967) that extensive use of 2,4-D in sugar cane has resulted in a decline of broad-leaved weeds and that these have been largely replaced by various grasses, especially birdseed-grass, *Panicum fasciculatum*. More recent herbicides have controlled these and they in their turn have been replaced by sedges e.g. *Cyperus diffusus*. A similar sequence has also occurred in Hawaii (Hanson 1959) where, in addition, the development of resistance in a dicotyledonous weed, *Erechtites hieracifolia*, to 2,4-D has been recorded in some sugar estates following several years repeated spraying of this herbicide.

In Britain the pattern is apparently similar. Comments made by crop husbandry specialists of the National Agricultural Advisory Service in response to an inquiry made specifically for this paper are remarkably consistent. They all indicate that whilst the species which are most susceptible to the herbicides commonly used in cereal crops, particularly *Sinapis arvensis,* common poppy, *Papaver rhoeas* and corn buttercup, *Ranunculus arvensis*, have greatly diminished and are now seldom important, many of the more tolerant dicotyledonous annuals are as frequent as hitherto or have even increased. Examples of the latter are: common chickweed, *Stellaria media*, common knotgrass, *Polygonum aviculare*, black bindweed, *P. convolvulus*, redshank, *P. persicaria*, speedwells, *Veronica* spp., hemp-nettles, *Galeopsis* spp. and fat-hen, *Chenopodium album*. This is broadly in agreement with the conclusions of Evans (1966).

Information from surveys

A few detailed surveys on the occurrence of weeds in arable land have been reported, which give detailed information of changes in weeds during the past two decades. The role of herbicides is implied but direct evidence is lacking because this can only be obtained by means of long-term experiments, a few examples of which are discussed later.

Weed surveys involving 3,200 observations on arable land were carried out in southern Germany during 1948-55 and 1958-65 (Bachthaler 1967). These showed that a reduction in the annual weeds that could easily be controlled by herbicides occurred during this period. This was accompanied by an increase of grasses particularly *Agropyron repens*, annual meadow-grass, *Poa annua*, and *Avena fatua*.

A comprehensive survey of weeds in 2,088 fields cropped with spring cereals was carried out in 1962-64 in Finland (Mukula *et al.* 1969). In this, each field was visited by a weed specialist who listed the weeds present. The ten most frequent species included a number of herbicide-tolerant annuals common in Britain, for example; *Stellaria media*, pale persicaria, *Polygonum lapathifolium*, and *P. convolvulus*. However, the second most widespread species was *Chenopodium album* which is susceptible to many herbicides. Treacle mustard, *Erysimum cheiranthoides*, was also found to be very widespread in spite of the ease with which it is killed by virtually all common herbicides used in cereals. The authors concluded that the use of the herbicide MCPA had apparently reduced the plant numbers of suceptible species, e.g. *Chenopodium*, *Galeopsis* and *Erysimum*, but had led to an apparent increase in resistant species including *Agropyron repens*, *Tripleurospermum maritimum* and field forget-me-not, *Myosotis arvensis*.

A large scale survey by means of questionnaires was carried out in the United States during 1959-62 to obtain information on the changing weed pattern in agronomic crops (USDA 1965). This

TABLE I

The most frequent dicotyledonous weeds recorded in four surveys in Britain

Survey Author	Dadd	Elliott, Cox & Simonds	North (Evans 1969)	Fisons Pest Control	
Year of observations ..	1962	1967	1967	1967	
Crop	Cereals	Cereals	Spring Barley	Spring Cereals	
Location	E.Anglia	E.Anglia	E.Anglia	Countrywide	
Description of data ..	% of fields (179) where weed is >4% of population	% occurrence in 104 fields	% occurrence in 31 fields	% of surveyed acreage infested	
				Heavy infestaation	Light infestaation
Sinapis arvensis ..	47	44	51	33	36
Stellaria media ..	46	43	97	53	30
Polygonum convolvulus	33	25	87	35	31
Veronica spp.	32	5	74	15	25
Polygonum aviculare ..	29	38	65	42	31
Tripleurospermum maritimum	29	38	42	13	25
Chenopodium album ..	25	7	55	13	30
Polygonum persicaria ..	20	14	26	24	21
Cirsium arvense ..	18	11	—	8	24
Galium aparine.. ..	17	24	35	12	23
Galeopsis spp.	11	—	—	11	12
Fumaria officinalis ..	8	1	—	4	21

revealed that several distinct groups of weeds were becoming increasingly serious problems in crop production. In order of decreasing importance these were: annual grasses, annual and perennial sedges, perennial grasses, deep-germinating annual broad-leaved weeds and perennial broad-leaved weeds. These changes are attributed to lack of hand-hoeing, reduced cultivations and increased reliance on selective herbicides.

In Britain, four surveys of weeds in cereal crops provide valuable information on the frequency of different weeds. They are summarised in Table I.

A survey of 179 fields carried out in 1962 by the National Agricultural Advisory Service (NAAS) in the Eastern Counties (Dadd 1962) showed that the most common weeds were the more herbicide-resistant dicotyledons, including *Stellaria media* and the common species of *Polygonum*. However, the herbicide-sensitive *Sinapis arvensis*, *Chenopodium album* and creeping thistle, *Cirsium arvense*, were still very common at this time.

Information relating to the same area was obtained by North during 1967 and by Elliott, Cox and Simonds (1968). The former was based on a series of NAAS herbicide trials (Evanş 1969) and the latter on field inspection cards obtained in 1967 for 140 fields of cereals. The results of both surveys indicated that little change had taken place since 1962, although the area is one in which annual herbicide usage on cereals is almost universal.

The only really extensive survey of the occurrence of weeds in cereals has been that undertaken by Fisons Pest Control in 1967 (Fisons 1968). In this, 8,500 fields were inspected in the spring and the weeds recorded. In addition some 8,000 replies to a questionnaire were received from farmers. Whilst the results cannot be considered in detail here, it will be seen from Table I that there is general agreement with those of the other surveys. The continuing survival of *Sinapis arvensis* is of particular interest in view of the marked susceptibility of this species to modern herbicides and the observations quoted earlier of its apparent decline.

These surveys were particularly concerned with dicotyledonous weeds because of the difficulties in identification of grasses in the young stages. However, another survey by Fisons Pest Control (1969) carried out in 1964, 1966 and 1968 was specifically concerned with *Avena fatua* in Eastern England. The survey was made prior to cereal harvest by means of roadside observations of some 5,000 fields of wheat and barley. Comparing the results for each of the 3 years it appears that in general the incidence of wild-oats diminished slightly during this period. The decline ranged from 3 to 7% in the crops recorded and may be attributed to the increase in the use of specific herbicides for the control of wild-oats. It should be noted that fields sprayed with these herbicides were included in the survey. However, in a few counties this survey indicated a marked increase in wild-oats during the 5 year period. The spread of wild oats into areas not previously affected has been noted elsewhere, e.g. Long (1968).

Long-term experiments and observations

1. *Arable weeds*

Records over a period of 12 years obtained by Ubrizsy (1968) in Hungary, show that regular use of triazine herbicides in maize reduced weed cover by 13-37%. Similarly, the use of growth regulator herbicides in winter wheat caused reductions of 9-25%. The species composition of the weed flora changed, the indigenous species tended to be replaced by common cosmopolitan weeds. Herbicide-resistant species became more prevalent.

An experiment in Germany is reported by Koch (1964) in which the absence of any form of weed control in three successive spring cereal crops was compared with annual herbicide treatment and with harrowing. The herbicide (2,4-D) significantly reduced broad-leaved weeds and led to an increase in blackgrass, *Alopecurus myosuroides*. In contrast, harrowing resulted in a small overall decline in the weed population, compared with the control plots, without affecting its composition.

In Britain the most significant data are those from the Broadbalk experiment at Rothamsted (Thurston 1969) in which the population of viable weed seeds in the soil has been determined in respect of different treatments as the criterion of the changing weed flora.

Over a period of 7 years continuous winter wheat, annual treatment by various herbicides was compared with no weed control apart from a 1-year fallow after 5 years. There was no change in the number of weed species present under either management. However, individual weed species did change substantially in density. The susceptible *Ranunculus arvensis* and common vetch, *Vicia sativa* declined markedly as a result of spraying whereas the herbicide-resistant species *Tripleurospermum maritimum* and *Alopecurus myosuroides* were not reduced but indeed increased.

In a long-term herbicide trial which was carried out at the Ministry of Agriculture's Experimental Husbandry Farm at Martyr Worthy near Winchester from 1951-1963 (Bridgets 1963), an arable rotation was followed which contained a high proportion of cereal crops, each receiving annual treatment by one of the following herbicides: DNOC, MCPA and 2,4-D. There were unsprayed control plots. Although no detailed assessments of weed populations were made, it was reported that by 1962 (after 11 years) the unsprayed plots carried large numbers of *Chenopodium album*, *Sinapis arvensis* and *Stellaria media*, also to a lesser extent, *Cirsium arvense*, and *Convolvulus arvensis*, whilst the herbicide-treated plots contained mainly *Stellaria media* and grass weeds. As all plots were managed similarly apart from the herbicide treatment it may be assumed that the latter was responsible for the diminished incidence of susceptible weeds.

2. *Grassland weeds*

In contrast to arable crops, the use of herbicides in grassland has remained comparatively static in Britain and only a very small fraction of the total acreage is sprayed. Although there is evidence from numerous authors e.g. Ubrizsy (1968) and Gutsell (1962) that even a single application of MCPA or 2,4-D can result in a long-lasting decline of susceptible species, the floristic composition of grassland swards is so much affected by management practices that the effects of herbicides on the weed flora cannot usefully be considered except where the management remains constant, a rare occurrence in agriculture.

The long-term suppressive effect of 2,4-D on dicotyledons in grassland, well known to gardeners who use this herbicide on lawns, has been studied in some detail in Hungary by Ubrizsy (1968). Two applications a year for three successive years reduced the ground cover of weeds in pasture by 50-60% and the number of weed species from 42 to 12. The results were long-lasting.

A unique series of plots on roadside verges near Bibury in Gloucestershire on which different treatments have been applied annually since 1958 demonstrates the response of vegetation of grassy habitats to repeated spraying. Willis (1969) describes how annual treatments with the selective herbicide 2,4-D, resulted in a marked reduction in dicotyledonous species and how, in plots that were not sprayed again after four initial annual treatments, this reduction was still largely evident seven years later. In contrast, on plots sprayed annually with the growth-suppressing chemical maleic hydrazide (which is mainly active on grasses) not only was the diversity of dicotyledonous species maintained, but at the end of a 10-year period, the number of species was two more than on the untreated controls.

Weed surveys carried out in fields at WRO

When the Weed Research Organization was set up in 1960 at Begbroke Hill Farm a survey was made of the weed flora in all the fields. This practice has been continued as far as possible year by year. The purpose has been to assist in the location of experiments should particular weed species be required. From these weed surveys the data from two fields have been selected for this paper. One field had originally been in permanent pasture and the other in continuous arable cropping.

The previous owner of the farm had not used herbicides at all and had kept half the fields as permanent grass and half as arable (roots and cereals). Initially therefore there were on the farm two weed floras, which were characteristic of these regimes.

In each field a series of transects at 20 yd intervals was marked out and across them a similar series. At each intersection a one square-ft quadrat was placed and the seedlings of dicotyledonous weeds within its area were then identified and counted. The same transects are used year by year so that the quadrats in separate years are placed as far as possible on the same spot. Grasses have not been included in the survey because of difficulties of identification in the youngest stages, but *Poa annua* has been frequent in both fields. The soil in both fields is a light sandy loam overlying gravel.

1. *Boddington Barn Field*

Prior to acquiring the farm in 1960 the field is thought to have been a permanent pasture for some time, possibly since the last war, when part of it at least was almost certainly ploughed. Since 1960 the field has been in a mostly arable rotation (Table II). The area of Boddington Barn Field surveyed is 12·23 acres and has been assessed by 148 quadrats on each occasion. The numbers of the principal species counted in these quadrats in seven separate years are given in Table III.

TABLE II

Cropping and herbicides used in the two fields at WRO since 1960

Year			Boddington Barn Field		Upper Begbroke Ground	
			Crop	Spray	Crop	Spray
1960 ..	..	..	Grass	—	Barley	dinoseb
1961 ..	..	..	Wheat	mecoprop	Barley	dinoseb
1962 ..	..	..	Expts	dicamba/ mecoprop/ MCPA	Grass	—
1963 ..	..	..	Expts	—	Grass	—
1964 ..	..	..	Barley & Oats	MCPA/ dicamba	Wheat	mecoprop
1965 ..	..	..	Barley	mecoprop	Expts	—
1966 ..	..	..	Oats	mecoprop	Barley	dinoseb/ MCPA
1967 ..	..	..	Oats	—	Barley	dinoseb/ mecoprop
1968 ..	..	..	Potatoes	paraquat/ linuron	—	—
1969 ..	..	..	Wheat	—	—	—

2. *Upper Begbroke Ground*

In contrast to Boddington Barn Field, Upper Begbroke Ground had been in arable cultivation for several years before 1960. In the absence of any herbicides the predominantly arable weed flora had built up to a fairly serious level. The area assessed in four separate years is 7·69 acres, which was assessed by 93 quadrats (Table IV).

The data presented for these two fields give a useful indication of the changes occurring in their weed populations, although how far these changes are due to herbicides is impossible to say, for climate, cultivations, fertiliser usage and crops have all had an influence.

The density of weeds in Upper Begbroke Ground which started at 1·5 million/acre was reduced by 82% in 6 years, whereas in Boddington Barn Field where the level was low to start with there

TABLE III

Weeds in Boddington Barn Field over 8 years

Species	1961	1964	1965	1966	1967	1968	1969
ethusa cynapium	25	180	140	53	11	109	59
erastium fontanum	85	131	50	33	24	0	20
maria officinalis	48	290	207	52	26	92	32
atricaria recutita	0	9	6	10	43	3	81
paver rhoeas	21	25	44	11	5	0	4
antago lanceolata	3	78	24	0	1	2	0
olygonum aviculare	1	176	118	10	33	51	78
olygonum convolvulus	1	139	148	0	6	47	20
anunculus bulbosus	119	7	79	63	74	4	6
enecio vulgaris	0	174	12	23	16	19	4
araxacum officinale agg.	41	11	58	1	1	0	0
rifolium repens	27	100	18	0	6	15	0
ther weeds	28	184	259	28	49	67	40
otal no. of weeds	399	1,504	1,253	284	259	409	344
otal no. of species	18	39	33	20	26	21	21
ean plants per acre	117,426	442,627	368,758	83,581	86,819	120,369	100,239
rable weeds (% of total)	28	76	75	64	62	95	91
rassland weeds (% of total)	50	14	17	24	28	5	2

has been only a 15% reduction in 8 years. These results confirm, what one would expect, that herbicides combined with good management reduce high density weed stands, but do little to eliminate low density populations. It is relevant to note that once a weed population has reached a very low level, spraying is less likely to be carried out.

Although the population density in Boddington Barn Field was only slightly reduced over the 8 years there were none-the-less very considerable changes in the species composition. Table III shows the changeover from a predominantly grassland weed flora with a residue of arable weeds from former cultivations to a more or less completely arable weed flora. This of course would presumably have occurred even without herbicides, but the relatively low density of arable weeds throughout the period must be due to good management, in which herbicides have undoubtedly played an important part. The weed flora in Upper Begbroke Ground although composed more or less entirely of arable weeds, exhibited considerable changes too, notably in the great decline of *Chrysanthemum segetum*, due possibly to the use of the very effective herbicide dinoseb aided by the field being two years under grass.

TABLE IV

Weeds in Upper Begbroke Ground over 6 years

Species	1961	1964	1966	1967
Chrysanthemum segetum ..	1,646	18	104	42
Aethusa cynapium	112	38	154	51
Stellaria media	746	190	398	142
Veronica spp.	200	45	121	34
Lamium amplexicaule ..	85	18	96	57
Raphanus raphanistrum ..	288	11	76	13
Polygonum convolvulus ..	118	0	88	5
Viola arvensis	124	108	232	100
Capsella bursa-pastoris ..	33	6	45	49
Legousia hybrida	21	21	90	65
Other weed species	185	283	205	75
Total no. of weeds	3,567	738	1,529	633
Total no. of species	23	21	25	27
Mean plants per acre	1,669,356	345,679	716,184	296,497

Although some grassland species present in Boddington Barn Field in 1961 were not recorded in 1969 there was in fact a total of three more weed species in 1969 than in 1961. Similarly in Upper Begbroke Ground there were four more species in 1967 than in 1961. In these instances it may be that reduction in numbers of the commoner species opened up the habitat, thereby allowing less-favoured species to become established.

Conclusions

The evidence reviewed in this paper, although very limited and often circumstantial, shows in general that the major effect of herbicide usage in arable fields is to reduce rather than to eliminate weed populations. Furthermore the relative frequency of individual species is altered. Contrary to popular belief it appears that even after some 20 years of intensive herbicide usage on British farms the most sensitive species such as *Sinapis arvensis*, although greatly diminished in numbers, occur as widely as before.

One of the difficulties in drawing firm conclusions from the data available is that in the absence of specific experiments, the effects of herbicides are invariably confounded with changes in all other factors relating to crops and crop and soil management. For example the use of nitrogenous fertilisers has greatly increased during the period under review (Rothamsted 1966). The introduction of new crop varieties has also undoubtedly favoured some weeds and discouraged others. Cultivation practices have also changed and these by themselves can have profound effects upon the success or otherwise of individual weeds. In recent years the reduction of soil cultivation in arable land has provided a markedly different and sometimes much less favourable environment for annual weeds, although in contrast perennials may be encouraged.

Grassland, although only infrequently sprayed up to the present, is likely to receive more herbicide treatment in the future along with more intensive management in general. It is clear from the evidence presented here that if herbicides such as 2,4-D are used, the results will contrast with those from arable land in that a reduction in the number of broad-leaved weeds will undoubtedly follow and this will be persistent. However, it may be possible to retain species of value by judicious selection of herbicides.

Turning to the future, two questions are often asked: (i) will weeds in agricultural crops be eventually eradicated by the continuing use of herbicides and (ii) are weeds likely to become resistant to herbicides in the same way that some insects and pathogenic organisms have become resistant to insecticides and antibiotics?

Most weeds of cultivated land are well adapted to survive long periods of adverse conditions by a variety of means, of which seed dormancy is the most important. Roberts (1962, 1968) found that if all seeding of weeds was prevented in a vegetable crop rotation, the viable weed seed population in the soil decreased at about 45% per year. If a half-life of the order of 1 year were general, then even after 7 years of complete weed control there would still be about 1% of the original seeds remaining: for a light weed infestation of, for example, 2 million seeds per acre, the 20,000 residue after this period would be more than sufficient to start up a new infestation should a lapse in management permit the weeds to set seed once again.

Complete weed control over long periods is virtually unattainable in practice, principally through periodic failure either partial or complete of weed control methods. Furthermore the law of diminishing returns sooner or later influences the farmer's attitude towards weeds, as has been discussed by Evans (1969). For as a field becomes less weedy the farmer begins to question whether his expenditure on weed control is any longer justified and sooner or later he will decide to discontinue his spraying programme. The decline of the weed population will then be at an end. It is therefore highly unlikely that annual weeds will ever disappear from fields. It is perhaps worth pointing out that weed seeds are continually being brought into fields in crop seed and straw, also by other agencies.

Control measures for perennial weeds whether chemical or cultural are also notoriously dependent on good management and weather. The cost of control is frequently high and all the trends are that the perennial weed problem in Britain will get worse before it gets better. The risks of minimum-tillage practices in encouraging perennial grass weeds has been emphasised by Whybrew (1968).

Will weeds become resistant to herbicides? The development of resistance in *Erechtites* to 2,4-D in Hawaii has already been noted and the existence of herbicide-tolerant strains within populations of weeds is well known (e.g. Switzer 1957; Rochecouste 1962; Evans & Pfeiffer 1967). Whilst the chances of resistance developing might at first sight seem high, the wealth of herbicides available, each with varying modes of action and effectiveness against different species, in combination with crop rotation are powerful arguments why this is unlikely to become a serious problem. The topic has been admirably discussed by Harper (1956).

The general conclusions from the evidence presented is that whilst the trend for the more herbicide-sensitive species to decline will continue, it is very probable that populations of more resistant or better-adapted species will continue to be maintained or even to increase in the face of continuing herbicide usage. Species with short life cycles and prolonged seed dormancy will be the most likely to thrive; rhizomatous perennials also. In addition the overall success of weeds will depend as much on the profitability of agriculture and horticulture as on the introduction of new types of herbicides for, throughout the history of agriculture, it has always been the prosperous farmer who has been prepared to spend more on keeping his fields clean than the farmer who has had to cut back expenditure wherever possible to obtain a profit.

Whatever the future holds in store, it is desirable that changes in weed populations should be better recorded than in the past. Can the B.S.B.I. help? If any member has any suggestions to this end we should very much like to hear about them. In the meantime at the Weed Research Organization through the generous co-operation of agricultural merchants and chemical manufacturers we shall continue to utilize their very extensive crop inspection records made during advisory visits to farms and to explore such other sources of information as are open to us.

Acknowledgement

We wish to thank the many members of the National Agricultural Advisory Service who were kind enough to help us in our enquiries, and Fisons Ltd. for permission to quote unpublished data.

References

ABERG, E. (1957). Weed control research and development in Sweden. *Proc. Br. Weed Control Conf.* 3rd, 141-164.

BACHTHALER, G. (1967). Changes in arable weed infestation with modern crop husbandry techniques. *Abstr. int. Congr. Pl. Prot. Vienna* 6th, 167-168.

BRIDGETS, E. H. F. (1963). *Rep. Bridgets expl. Husb. Fm* 1963, 9-10.

DADD, C. V. (1962). Weed control in cereals. A review. *Proc. Br. Weed Control Conf.* 6th, 123-140.

ELLIOTT, J. G., COX, T. W. and SIMONDS, J. S. W. (1968). A survey of weeds and their control in cereal crops in south East Anglia during 1967. *Proc. Br. Weed Control Conf.* 9th, 200-207.

EVANS, E. and PFEIFFER, R. K. (1967). Selective phytotoxicity of 2,4-dichloro-6 (o-chloroanilino)-s-triazine ('Dyrene') to *Cirsium arvense*. *Nature, Lond.* **215**, 782-783.

EVANS, S. A. (1966) A review of the present position in cereal weed control. and an introduction to research reports. *Proc. Br. Weed Control Conf.* 8th, 753-763.

EVANS, S. A. (1969). Spraying of cereals for the control of weeds. *Expl. Husb.* **18**, 103-109.

FISONS LTD. (1968). Broad-leaved weed infestations in cereals. *Fisons agric. tech. Inf. (Spring)* 21-28.

FISONS LTD. (1969). Personal Communication.

GUTSELL, R. J. (1962). Field experience in combining MPCA & fertilisers for the control of *Ranunculus* spp. (buttercup) in permanent pasture. *Proc. Br. Weed Control Conf.* 6th, 105-119.

HANSON, N. S. (1959). Chemical weed control in Hawaii. *Proc. 10th Cong. Int. Soc. Sug. Cane Technol.* 538-549.

HARPER, J. L. (1956). The evolution of weeds in relation to resistance to herbicides. *Proc. Br. Weed Control Conf.* 3rd, 179-188.

HAY, R. J. (1968). The changing weed problem in the prairies. *Agric. Inst. Rev.* **23**, 17-19.

KOCH, W. (1964). Some observations on changes in weed populations under continuous cereal cropping and with different methods of weed control. *Weed Res.* **4**, 351-356.

LONG, E. (1968). The wild oat bogy moves south-west. *Fmrs Wkly* **69**, 90.

MUKULA, J., RAATIKAINEN, M., LALLUKKA, R. and RAATIKAINEN T. (1969). Composition of weed flora in spring cereals in Finland. *Annls agric. Fenn.* **8**, 59-110.

NEW SOUTH WALES DEPARTMENT OF AGRICULTURE (1967). *Rep. Dep. Agric. N.S.W.* 1956-66, 25.

PETERS, R. A. (1967). Changes in the weed population when using a single herbicide in maize monoculture. *Abstr. int. Congr. Pl. Prot. Vienna* 6th, 382-383.

ROBERTS, H. A. (1962). Studies on the weeds of vegetable crops. II. Effect of six years of cropping on the weed seeds in the soil. *J. Ecol.* **50**, 803-813.

ROBERTS, H. A. (1968). The changing population of viable weed seeds in an arable soil. *Weed Res.* **8**, 253-256.

ROCHECOUSTE, E. (1962). Studies on the biotypes of *Cynodon dactylon* (L.) Pers. II. Growth response to trichloroacetic and 2,2-dichloropropionic acids. *Weed Res.* **2**, 136-145.

ROTHAMSTED (1966). *Rep. Rothamsted expl Stn* 1966.

SWITZER, C. M. (1957). The existence of 2,4-D resistant strains of wild carrot. *Proc. N. East Weed Control Conf.* 11th, 315-318.

TATE & LYLE LTD. (1967). *Rep. Tate & Lyle Res. Centre* 1967, 270-271.

THURSTON, J. M. (1969). Weed studies in Broadbalk. *Rep. Rothamsted expl. Stn* 1968, 186-208.

UBRIZSY, G. (1968). Long-term experiments on the flora-changing effect of chemical weedkillers in plant communities. *Acta. agron. Hung.* **17**, 171-193.

U.S. DEPARTMENT OF AGRICULTURE (1965). *A survey of extent and cost of weed control and specific weed problems.* Publ. U.S. Dept. Agric. Wash., ARS 34-23-1.

WAY, J. M. (Ed.) (1969). *Road Verges, Their Function and Management.* Nature Conservancy, Monks Wood Experimental Station.

WILLIS, A. J. (1969). Road verges—experiments on the chemical control of grass and weeds. In Way J. M. (1969) 52-60.

WHYBREW, J. E. (1968). Experimental Husbandry Farm experience with herbicides and tillage systems for cereal growing. *N.A.A.S. q. Rev.* **80**, 154-160.

DISCUSSION

Mr. E. MILNE-REDHEAD asked whether there was a minimum concentration of weeds below which there was no loss in yield.

Mr FRYER replied that it is now rare to find weeds in cereal crops reducing yields: farmers would continue to spray because a weedy crop was more costly to harvest in a wet autumn than a clean one.

Mr J. E. LOUSLEY said he was still convinced that changes in cultivation had been more important than herbicides in reducing the weed population in the countryside. Ploughing before weeds flowered in the autumn and the ploughing and cropping of headlands both contributed. Annual fluctuations in the weed population in relation to management and season are so great that valid conclusions about permanent change could only result from long-term observations.

Mr FRYER agreeing, said that long-term observations would be needed on representative farms in different parts of the country. Observations must be made on seedlings and it would be necessary to train botanists to identify weeds at this stage. Whilst locally, as yet, there were no apparent losses of species they might only be surviving on a residual stock of seed in the soil. This was something which ought to be watched.

AIR POLLUTION AND ITS EFFECTS ON PLANTS

H. J. M. Bowen

Department of Chemistry,
The University, Reading

Introduction

In this paper I propose to distinguish between contamination and pollution as follows. The release of substances into the air so that their subsequent concentrations are measurable will be called *contamination*, while the term *pollution* will be reserved for situations where the substances concerned have measurable effects on living organisms.

The vast majority of atmospheric contamination in Britain to-day, and in the past, has arisen from burning fossil fuels. Britain has a much longer history of atmospheric contamination than any other country. Parliament passed an act prohibiting the burning of coal in London in 1273, but by Tudor times this had evidently been forgotten. Atmospheric contamination became serious on a nation-wide scale around 1830 with the start of the Industrial Revolution, and from then until 1914 there was a continuous yearly increase in the amount of coal burnt in this country. Between 1920 and 1932 production (and consumption) fell off owing to foreign competitors, but then increased again to a maximum in 1955, when large amounts of coal were imported for the first time. At present the amount of coal burnt is declining, but this is more than offset by the phenomenal rise in imported crude petroleum, which began about 1948 and which shows no sign of levelling out.

The main contaminants

The main contaminants introduced into the atmosphere by burning coal and oil are carbon dioxide, carbon monoxide, sulphur dioxide and smoke. These will be considered in turn.

1. *Carbon dioxide.* This is much the most abundant air contaminant produced by man's activities. In 1965 the estimated mass of carbon dioxide produced by combustion in Britain was 920 million tons, while that in the entire world was about 9,000 million tons (Bowen 1966). These large figures are seen in better perspective if it is made clear that the second of them corresponds to about $1\cdot3\%$ of the total carbon dioxide taken up by vegetation on the earth during photosynthesis. The extra carbon dioxide is measurable. The concentration of carbon dioxide in the atmosphere has risen from 570 mg m^{-3} in 1900 to 645 mg m^{-3} in 1960, a rise of about 14% (Junge 1963). It can be shown that a molecule of carbon dioxide

spends about four years in the atmosphere on average, before it is absorbed by the ocean or by green plants. At low concentrations, carbon dioxide is an important plant nutrient, and so the recent increase may be improving the efficiency of photosynthesis in some parts of the world. The extra carbon dioxide may also trap more infra-red radiation from the sun and so reduce the rate of loss of heat from the earth. At present one can only be thankful that this particular contaminant is not a pollutant in the sense used here.

2. *Carbon monoxide* is a less abundant contaminant, produced by incomplete combustion. The estimated amount produced in Britain in 1965 was 29 million tons, and its mean residence time in the atmosphere is probably a few months. The 'natural' concentration of carbon monoxide in the atmosphere is not known, since it was not observed until 1952. However, the substance is not very toxic to plants, compared with its high toxicity to mammals, and it is doubtful if the gas can be called a pollutant. It is possible that it contributes to the difficulty of growing trees in busy streets in large cities, where local concentrations of the gas may rise to $20\mu g\ m^{-3}$ or more, but other factors are probably also involved.

FIGURE 1

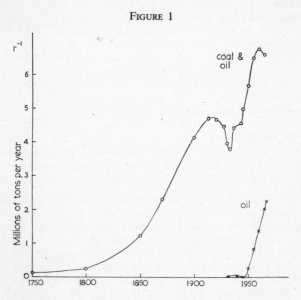

Sulphur dioxide emission in Britain in millions of tons per year, 1750-1960.

3. *Sulphur dioxide* is produced as by-product of burning coal and crude oil, since both of these fuels contain a few per cent of sulphur. It is not easy to find reliable analyses in the literature, but the mean sulphur content of 492 British coals was 1·208% (DSIR 1931 ; 1942). According to Greig (1958) the mean sulphur content of crude petroleum from the Middle East is 1·62%. From these figures, and from the published statistics of coal consumption (Wilson 1945, Board of Trade Statistics) and oil imports for Britain, Fig. 1 has been constructed. It represents the estimated annual quantities of sulphur dioxide liberated into the air in Britain between 1750 and 1965. In 1965 about 6·75 million tons of sulphur dixoide was produced in Britain, and recent measurements confirm that the amount is still rising (Commins and Walker 1967).

Sulphur dioxide is a global contaminant, but it is much more important as a local pollutant, since its mean residence time in the atmosphere is quite short. Recent estimates of this residence time lie between 11 hours and 4 days (Junge 1963, Meetham 1964) Its concentration near big cities is usually between 10 and 400 μg m⁻³, as against 0·1 μg m⁻³ in air over the Pacific Ocean. If the daily production of sulphur dioxide in Britain (nearly 20,000 tons) were uniformly distributed over the country in a layer of air 200m deep, as might occur during an inversion, the concentration of the gas would be 550μg m⁻³ or about 0·2 parts per million w/v. This would be serious pollution since 0·1-0·2 ppm is toxic to many plants (Thomas 1961).

FIGURE 2

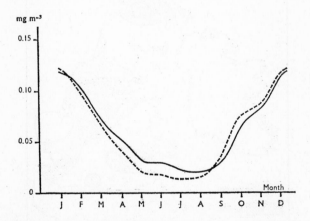

Mean monthly atmospheric pollution at Reading, Berks., 1962-1966.
- - - - - - - - =SO₂÷2; ——————=Smoke.

In practice, sulphur dioxide concentrations of this order of magnitude are found in and near most large industrial cities and in the vicinity of power stations. A notable feature is the seasonal variation of sulphur dioxide pollution: concentrations in the winter months (December to February) may be six times those during the summer (May to August) (Fig. 2). This is largely due to the greater frequency of inversions during the winter, but plant uptake may contribute to the decline during the spring. The net result is that the effects of sulphur dioxide are most pronounced on those plants which retain their photosynthetic cells above ground during the winter. Thus, evergreen trees, bryophytes and lichens are particularly prone to damage from sulphur dioxide.

Although the precise mode of toxicity of sulphur dioxide is still a matter of debate, its effects may be observed as leaf necrosis and increased rates of leaf senescence (Bleasdale 1959, Thomas 1961). Different plant species differ by a factor of about fifteen in the concentration of sulphur dioxide which they can tolerate without injury. A sensitive species, *Medicago sativa*, tolerated 0·14 ppm SO_2 in the atmosphere for 45 days without significant effects, but detectable effects were observed

FIGURE 3

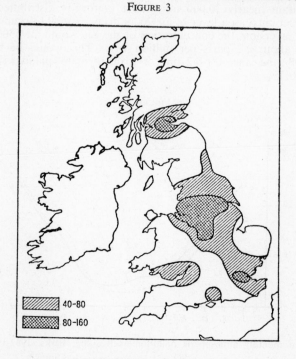

40-80

80-160

Mean amounts of sulphur dioxide in winter air, in micrograms per cubic metre. (After Meetham 1964).

at 0·19 ppm (Thomas and Hill 1937).   Fumigation experiments have been reviewed by Scurfield (1960).

Sulphur dioxide is proved or implicated as the main air pollutant causing damage to plant life in Britain.   Typical leaf necrosis symptoms are frequent on garden plants in towns. The sensitivity of evergreens is reflected in the need to move the National Pinetum from Kew to Bedgebury, Kent (Scurfield 1955) and in the failure to establish conifers on the more polluted Pennine moorlands.   I have suggested that the decline of native *Juniperus communis* in the midlands and north-east Britain may be a consequence of SO_2 pollution belts (Figs 3 & 4) (Bowen 1965).   Lichens, especially foliose and fruticose species, are notable indicators of sulphur dioxide pollution. Jones (1952) showed that corticolous species *(Evernia prunastri, Parmelia* spp., *Ramalina* spp., *Pertusaria* spp. and *Usnea* spp.) were especially sensitive to pollution in the Midlands and recent studies have showed that sulphur dioxide is the agent responsible. (Fig. 5; Gilbert 1965, Laundon 1967).   Thus Laundon (1967) has mapped the lichen zones of Greater London, from the centre where only one species survives, to the outer suburbs, and shown that they are better correlated with the concentra-

FIGURE 4

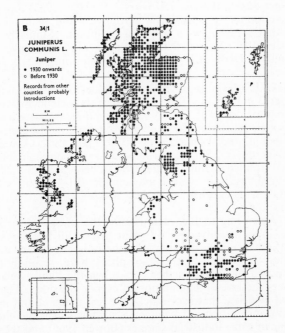

Distribution map of *Juniperus communis*.   Note extinctions in regions known to be highly polluted.

FIGURE 5

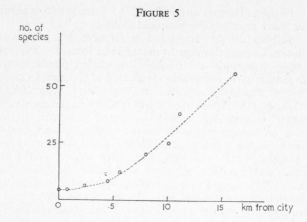

Distribution of lichens near Newcastle-upon-Tyne. (After Gilbert 1965).

tions of sulphur dioxide than with smoke levels. 97 out of 159 species of lichen recorded from the London area have become extinct during the last 150 years. Savidge (1963) reported the extinction of 67 species of bryophytes and many lichens in South Lancashire as a result of pollution. Similarly Hawksworth (1969) claims that 30 species of lichen have become extinct in Derbyshire owing to air pollution.

4. *Smoke* is the most obvious by-product of burning coal, and about 2 million tons are produced every year in Britain. The amount is declining, owing partly to public pressure and partly to tough legislation, as shown by figures for insoluble ash deposited in outer London (Fig. 6; Meetham 1964, Commins and Walker 1967). Smoke particles are local contaminants whose mean residence time in the atmosphere is about 20 hours. Contaminated air in cities may contain $0 \cdot 1$-4 mg m^{-3} of smoke particles, as against 50-100 μg m^{-3} of colloidal particles in 'pure' air.

According to Bleasdale (1959), the smoke near industrial cities may act adversely on plant growth in two ways. First the light available for photosynthesis is cut down, especially during the winter, by the atmospheric haze: secondly the soot deposited on leaves further cuts down the light available and lowers the rate of assimilation of carbon dioxide. There is no good evidence that soot blocks the leaf stomata and interferes with transpiration. Toxic metals such as nickel and chromium occur in some industrial smokes (Bowen 1966) and these could poison lichens and other plants, though there is no evidence that they have done so.

FIGURE 6

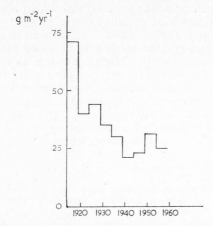

Insoluble ash deposited at Finsbury Park, London. (After D.S.I.R. 1960).

Other contaminants

Local pollution by fluorides has been observed near brickworks in the Midlands (Allcroft 1959) and near the aluminium extraction plant at Fort William, Inverness (Agate *et al.* 1949). The effects on plants are less severe in this country than those noted for animals grazing on the polluted vegetation.

Lead pollution from burning petrol containing lead tetraethyl has been found very locally near highways. Again, the effects on the plants themselves are trivial compared with the possible effects on grazing animals (Patterson 1965).

Air pollution by peroxyacetyl nitrate, which is a serious problem in Los Angeles (Darley *et al.* 1966), has not been definitely reported from Great Britain.

Cement dusts are local pollutants with harmful effects on plants, but there are few reports of toxic effects from this country (Darley 1966).

Radioactive contamination of the atmosphere from nuclear reactors has had no measurable effects on plants, and is unlikely to do so if current safety precautions are maintained (Stewart *et al.* 1958).

Future problems.

It is to be hoped that the gradual replacement of coal and oil by nuclear power will ultimately reduce the total amount of pollutants released to the atmosphere. Meanwhile the amount of sulphur dioxide in our air is the main worry, and this is now measured at stations throughout the country. In order to reduce the sulphur dioxide emitted, one can either purify the fuel or try to absorb the sulphur from the waste gases. The first alternative should be investigated more fully, because the second is only applicable to large installations such as power stations, and not to domestic users who constitute a source of pollution about as great as the whole of British Industry (Lucas 1958). At present it is not economic to remove much of the sulphur from waste gases, as sulphur dioxide is a cheap chemical. Higher chimneys do nothing to reduce the emission, they merely dissipate it over a wider area.

By a happy accident, most of the rarer bryophytes and lichens in this country inhabit the northern and western parts of these islands, which are the least subject to industrial pollution. It is to be hoped that current Government policy of attracting industry to these regions will not result in the further impoverishment of our flora.

REFERENCES

AGATE, J. N. et al. (1949). Industrial fluorosis. A study of the hazard to man and animals near Fort William, Scotland. Med. Res. Coun. Memo. No. 22. H.M.S.O., London.

ALLCROFT, R. (1959). Fluorosis in farm animals. Sympos. Inst. Biol. 8, 95-102.

BLEASDALE, J. K. A. (1959). The effects of air pollution on plant growth. Sympos. Inst. Biol. 8, 81-87.

BOWEN, H. J. M. (1965). Sulphur and the distribution of British plants. Watsonia 6, 114-119.

BOWEN, H. J. M. (1966). Trace Elements in Biochemistry. Academic Press.

BOWEN, H. J. M. (1968). The Flora of Berkshire. Privately published.

COMMINS, B. T. and WALKER, R. E. (1967). Observations from a ten-year study of pollution at a site in the city of London. Atmosph. Environment 1, 49-68.

DARLEY, E. F. (1966). Studies on the effect of cement-kiln dust on vegetation. J. Air Pollut. Control. Ass. 16, 145-150.

DARLEY, E. F., NICHOLS, C. W. and MIDDLETON, J.T. (1969). Identification of air pollution damage to agricultural crops. Bull. Calif. Dep. Agric. 55, 11-19.

D.S.I.R. (1931). Physical and Chemical Survey of National Coal Resources No. 2, H.M.S.O., London.

D.S.I.R. (1942). ibid., No. 55.

GILBERT, O. L. (1965). Lichens as indicators of air pollution in the Tyne valley. In Goodman G. T. et al. (Eds) (1965).

GOODMAN, G. T., EDWARDS, R. W. and LAMBERT, J. M. (Eds) (1965). Ecology and the Industrial Society. Oxford.

GREIG, D. A. (1958). Habitat of Oil. American Association of Petroleum Geologists.

HAWKSWORTH, D. L. (1969). The lichen flora of Derbyshire. Lichenologist 4, 105-193.

JONES, E. W. (1952). Some observations on the lichen flora of tree boles with special reference to the effect of smoke. Revue bryol. lichen. 21, 97-116.

JUNGE, C. E. (1963). Air Chemistry and Radioactivity. Academic Press.

LAUNDON, J. R. (1967). A study of the lichen flora of London. Lichenologist 3, 277-327.

LUCAS, D. H. (1958). The atmospheric pollution of cities. Int. J. Air Pollut. 1, 71-86.

MEETHAM, A. R. (1964). Atmospheric Pollution, Ed. 3. Oxford & London.

PATTERSON, C. C. (1965). Lead in the environment. Arch. Envir. Hlth 11, 344-364.

SAVIDGE, J. P. (Ed.) (1963). *Travis's Flora of South Lancashire.* Liverpool.
SCURFIELD, G. (1955). Atmospheric pollution considered in relation to horticulture. *J. R. hort. Soc.* **80**, 93-101.
SCURFIELD, G. (1960). Air pollution and tree growth. *For. Abstr.* **21**, 339-347.
STEWART, N. G., GALE, H. J. and CROOKS, R. N. (1958). The atmospheric diffusion of gases discharged from the chimney of the Harwell reactor BEPO. *Int. J. Air. Pollut.* **1**, 87-102.
THOMAS, M. D. and HILL, G. R. (1937). Relation of sulphur dioxide in the atmosphere to photosynthesis and respiration in alfalfa. *Pl. Physiol. Lancaster* **12**, 285-307.
THOMAS, M. D. (1961). Effects of air pollution on plants. In *Air Pollution.* World Hlth Organ. Monograph ser. No. 42, 233-278.
WILSON, H. (1945). *New Deal for Coal.* London.

DISCUSSION

Mr C. J. CADBURY asked whether East Anglia is more polluted than other areas of Britain.

Dr BOWEN replied that it was not so polluted as the central Midlands but that Essex must be in a high pollution area as it receives most of the SO2 fall-out from London. In contrast, north Norfolk would be relatively unpolluted.

Mr H. H. LAMB drew attention to the fact that although East Anglia lay down-wind of the prevailing westerlies, serious pollution was most likely to occur at times of inversion and light winds. These were usually associated with easterly winds so that the most polluted areas lay west of London rather than north east.

Mr D. McCLINTOCK asked whether car exhaust has any effect on roadside vegetation and whether any beneficial effects of pollution on plant life were known.

Dr BOWEN replied that roadside verges were mainly affected by fine mineral particles from the ground up road surface. A high incidence of SO2 might help reduce attacks from Black Spot on roses, and could, in areas with sulphur deficient soils such as Dakota, be a beneficial fertiliser.

Mr J. E. LOUSLEY asked whether there were pollutants from car exhaust in addition to lead, the effects of which were not yet appreciated.

Dr K. MELLANBY said that it had been calculated in America that half as much nitrate as was put on soil as fertiliser could come from exhausts eventually. This would surely have an effect on wild vegetation.

Mr H. H. LAMB commented that water is also a pollutant. Under inversion conditions during frost the atmosphere receives more water from industry, exhausts and so on than it can hold. This has lead to an increase in the number of freezing days in the Glasgow area and has increased the number of days with persistent fog and low temperatures along railway lines and motorways.

Dr D. P. YOUNG asked whether thermal pollution resulting from water heated by Atomic Power Stations could be serious.

Dr BOWEN admitted the effect but thought that the creation of new warm water conditions might create diversity and increase botanical interest.

THE LAST SEVENTY YEARS

F. H. PERRING

Nature Conservancy,
Monks Wood Experimental Station, Huntingdon

Types of change

When we talk of changes in our flora we normally mean either the increase of introduced, non-native species, or the decline of native species. In this paper I must be the pessimist and deal only with the latter. Nevertheless, in passing it must be said that the largest changes which have taken place, taking a bird's eye view, are the planting of exotic conifers for forestry and the sowing of introduced and bred strains of grasses and clovers for pasture and hay. During the same period our river banks have become Balsam highways covered with *Impatiens* spp., our mountain streams with *Epilobium nerterioides*, our lawns with *Veronica filiformis* and our paths with *Matricaria matricarioides*.

It is certain that these introductions are having an effect on the native flora: species of permanent pasture, for example, could become the rarities of the future. For the moment, however, I wish to deal with the rarities of today.

Survey of rare species distribution

Two years ago we began, at the Biological Records Centre, a survey of the current distribution of the rarest native species of flowering plants and ferns in the flora of Great Britain. This survey was carried out by Miss M. N. Hamilton with the collaboration of the County Recorders of the B.S.B.I. and numerous other correspondents, and I wish to express my gratitude to her and all of them for the very considerable task which was undertaken and fulfilled.

In the *Atlas of the British Flora* (Perring and Walters 1962) about 400 maps of species which occurred in 20 or fewer vice-counties are labelled A. In the preparation of these a thorough search was made of the literature and the main national herbaria, and, in addition, several botanists with wide experience were asked for their comments. In all cases the most recent record was sought. The records were supplemented by field records made between 1954 and 1960. By these means the rare species maps in the *Atlas* give a fairly accurate account of the number of 10 km squares in which each occurred in the period 1930-1960, and, in addition, the squares from which each had apparently disappeared.

We used these maps as an objective guide to the selection of the species to include in the present survey. The survey was conducted in two parts. In the first part all species occurring in 8 or fewer 10 km squares in Great Britain in 1930 were considered. This gave us 198 species. In the second part all species occurring in 9 to 15 10 km squares were added. This gave a further 76 species. In addition 4 species were included which had more than 15 squares in 1930-1960 but which were known to have declined rapidly. They were: *Linum anglicum* (18 squares), *Lathyrus palustris* (25), *Himanto-glossum hircinum* (70) and *Rhyncospora fusca* (18). This gave a total of 278 species in all.

The survey was intended to discover which species in our flora have populations now so small that they could be threatened with extinction. For this reason with the few exceptions mentioned above we have not looked at species with over 15 10 km squares in 1930, though we believe there may be a few others, e.g. *Bupleurum rotundifolium*, which have declined very rapidly in the last 40 years, which should also be included. The survey has conservation as its ultimate objective. It was confined to Great Britain, because, within this area there is now established a local conservation organisation in each county upon whom the task of considering the conservation of hundreds of small sites must inevitably fall. We should willingly now carry out a similar survey in collaboration with Irish botanists, for in Ireland, in the last few years, the growth of interest in conservation has been extremely rapid. In selecting the species to be surveyed the Channel Isles records were ignored because floristically these islands lie outside the British Isles. If these records had been considered a number of species which are very rare on the mainland of Great Britain would have been omitted from the survey.

Results of the rare species survey

1. *All species.* The survey for the *Atlas* and the current survey make a valid comparison possible of the number of 10 km squares from which the species were known in 1930 and 1960. Further, if we assume that no native species ever increases its number of localities (the survey confirms that this is true except for some orchids and ruderal species) and that all localities known were therefore extant when recording began about 1600, we can add a third point in time. The first comparison we can make is of the total change in the number of squares for the 278 species over the period. In 1600 there were 3,390 species/square records: by 1930 this had fallen to 1,673 (49%), and by 1960 to 1,176 (35%).

10 km squares may contain several localities. During the *Atlas* survey the squares only were required, though in many instances the more exact data were abstracted. For the current survey the number of localities has been asked for. The figures for localities are less reliable than those for squares because of the difficulty of consistency in defining a locality. In addition there is the possibility of the same locality appearing under two or more different names in the past. Sorting these out could cause a big decline in localities but no decline in the species. In 1600 there were 4,595 species/

locality records: by 1950 this had fallen to 1902 (41%) and by 1960 to 1,425 (31%).

Whilst the final figure from squares and localities is probably too low because a thorough search of all the old localities would show that some of them are still extant, I think it is reasonable to assume that the present number of localities of our 278 rarest species is only about one third of what it once was.

It is dangerous I know to use these slender figures to project forwards but, if the present apparent rate of loss continued (about 15 10 km squares per annum) the majority of these species would be extinct or nearly so by the year 2050.

2. *Extinctions*. Since recording began 20 native species are believed to have become extinct in Great Britain, an average of one every 18 years. Some loss is inevitable: some may be due to subtle biological causes beyond our understanding to control, but the

TABLE I

Extinctions from the flora of Great Britain 1600–1969

S=Channel Islands   H=Ireland.

	Last record	S	H	Probable cause
1800-1900				
Scirpus hudsonianus..	1808	—	—	Drainage
Carex davalliana ..	1831	—	—	Drainage and building
Centaurium latifolium	1871	—	—	Collecting
Senecio palustris ..	1899	—	—	Drainage
S. paludosus	19th C.	—	—	Drainage
Rubus arcticus ..	19th C.	—	—	Not known
Saxifraga rosacea ..	19th C.	—	+	Not known
1900-1930				
Pinguicula alpina ..	1909	—	—	Not known
Euphorbia pilosa ..	1924	—	—	Not known
Holosteum umbellatum	1924	—	—	Habitat destroyed
1930-1940				
Halimione pedunculata	1934	—	—	Not known
Otanthus maritimus	1936	—	+	Not known
Polygonum maritimum	1936	—	—	Partially habitat destroyed
1940-1950				
Spiranthes aestivalis	1947	—	—	Collecting and drainage
Campanula persicifolia	1949	—	—	Habitat destroyed
1950-1960				
Elodea nuttallii ..	1950	—	+	Not known
Euphorbia peplis ..	1950	+	—	Habitat change
Galeopsis segetum ..	1957	—	—	Habitat change
Spergularia bocconi	1959	+	—	Not known
1960-1970				
Bupleurum falcatum	1962	—	—	Habitat change

majority are due to man, and the evidence is that his destructive effect on the flora is accelerating, as the figures in Table I disclose. In the 300 years before 1900 only 7 species are known to have been lost, though the last dates are all in the 19th Century: in the 70 years since 1900 thirteen species have become extinct, and the current rate of loss is one species every 4 years. This change in rate may not be as bad as it seems.   Several species could have occurred in Britain in 1600 which were destroyed before they were ever seen by botanists: therefore the apparent absence of extinctions in the 17th and 18th centuries may be significant as an absence of observers rather than an absence of change.   Some extinctions may recur, particularly the sea-shore species *Euphorbia peplis*, *Halimione pedunculata*, *Polygonum maritimum* and *Spergularia bocconi*, and is everyone certain that *Spiranthes aestivalis* does not still occur in the New Forest?

3. *Very rare species.*   It is clear that the rate of extinction is increasing, but so too is the number of species which are restricted to only one or two localities.   If we consider the rare species (excluding extinctions) and the number of squares from which they were known in 1900, 1930 and 1960 the most striking change is in the number of species which now occur in only 1 or 2 squares. Before 1900 only 44 (17·4%) of the rare species occurred in 1 or 2 squares.   By 1930 this had risen to 59 (23·3%).   In the last 30-40 years the number has increased to 97 (38·7%).   49 of the species occur in only one square whilst the remaining 47 occur in two.

The species which had only 1 or 2 squares before 1900 and have survived with these small populations for a large period are mainly those which are at the edge of their range in Great Britain and occur in special habitats.   33 of the 97 species are confined to the south and south west where they occur in naturally open habitats: sea-cliffs, cliff-tops, and sand-dunes, or in similar areas inland.   17 species occur in Scotland or northern England where many of them are arctic-alpine relics, also surviving in open habitats on cliff or scree.   A further 11 species in this group occur in scattered localities in England and Wales.   These species have survived for so long for two reasons.   First the habitat is often one which cannot be easily destroyed by ploughing, draining or afforestation, and secondly, as these species are traditional rarities, those involved in conservation are likely to be already aware of the importance of their localities and one hopes have already taken some steps to protect them.   We must of course be concerned about the future of these species, but their immediate future does not seem so bleak as it is for those species which have been declining rapidly over the last 60 or 70 years to reach a position where only one or two localities now remain.

In Table II the species which fall into this category are arranged in groups which are determined by the main most likely cause of their decline.   By far the biggest threat comes from agriculture;

TABLE II
Very rare species which have declined rapidly

Probable cause	Squares			Localities		
	1900	1930	1960	1900	1950	1960
Changes in arable farming						
Anthoxanthum puelii	62	9	2	69	9	2
Bromus interruptus	21	11	1	76	1	1
Lythrum hyssopifolia	37	5	1	51	3	2
Polycarpon tetraphyllum	14	5	2	15	6	6
Rhinanthus serotinus	71	10	2	83	6	2
Veronica triphyllos	23	5	2	29	5	3
V. verna	8	3	2	8	3	2
Ploughing						
Armeria elongata	6	2	1	6	2	1
Artemisia campestris	11	12	2	15	3	2
Eryngium campestre	22	12	2	33	6	2
Gnaphalium luteo-album	6	4	1	7	4	2
Juncus capitatus	8	4	1	9	2	1
Scorzonera humilis	3	3	1	3	2	1
Drainage						
Galium debile	5	5	2	7	5	3
Liparis loeselii	27	12	2	38	11	2
Scheuchzeria palustris	9	3	1	9	1	1
Selinum carvifolia	5	3	2	5	3	2
Viola stagnnia	15	7	2	21	3	3
Collecting						
Cyclamen hederifolium	4	2	1	6	2	1
Cypripedium calceolus	19	3	1	24	1	1
Gentiana nivalis	4	3	2	4	3	2
Lychnis alpina	3	3	2	5	3	2
Minuartia rubella	5	3	2	6	3	2
Scrub and Woodland Management						
Carex depauperata	6	3	2	8	2	2
Euphorbia corallioides	4	4	1	4	2	1
Lack of Management						
Ranunculus ophioglossifolius	4	3	1	4	3	2
Natural Causes						
Crepis foetida	16	4	1	24	3	2
Elatine hydropiper	9	4	2	16	4	2
Matthiola incana	4	4	1	6	2	1
M. sinuata	16	1	1	18	2	1
Orchis militaris	18	1	2	29	2	2
O. simia	8	3	2	11	5	3
Orobanche picridis	22	5	1	24	3	1
Spartina alterniflora	4	1	1	4	1	1

by the destruction of the habitat by ploughing or drainage, or by changes in agricultural practice which has affected the species of arable fields in particular.

The next biggest known threat is from collecting and digging up. For five species observers suggest that this is the most likely

TABLE III

Species showing major declines from over 20 squares in 1900 to less than
10 squares at the present day

Probable cause	Squares			Localities		
	1900	1930	1960	1900	1950	1960
Changes in arable farming						
Arnoseris minima	74	13	3	79	9	3
Filago apiculata ..	59	10	7	65	21	11
Melampyrum arvense	39	12	5	47	11	5
Ploughing						
Carex montana	26	14	8	33	13	9
Corynephorus canescens	22	14	4	25	12	4
Gentianella germanica ..	26	14	8	44	26	18
Salvia pratensis ..	29	13	4	36	11	7
Drainage						
Damasonium alisma	49	8	3	90	9	3
Lathyrus palustris	40	25	3	48	12	3
Leersia oryzoides	20	10	7	23	8	8
Oenanthe silaifolia	40	13	9	48	15	9
Pulicaria vulgaris	95	12	7	167	7	8
Stratiotes aloides..	51	15	9	65	20	10
Teucrium scordium	22	5	3	24	4	3
Scrub and Woodland Management						
Cynoglossum germanicum	50	6	6	58	7	6
Dryopteris cristata	26	10	3	26	8	3
Lithospermum purpurocaeuleum	22	13	4	29	11	4
Natural Causes						
Himantoglossum hircinum	88	70	3	118	13	4
Lotus angustissimus	36	10	3	40	9	4
Verbascum pulverulentum	23	9	9	36	16	9

cause of decline. All of them are species of what would normally
be regarded as reasonably safe habitats: *Cyclamen hederifolium* and
Cypripedium calceolus in woods, whilst *Gentiana nivalis*, *Lychnis
alpina* and *Minuartia rubella* are species more or less confined to
rock-ledges.

Changes in woodland management and scrub clearance may
account for the decline of *Carex depauperata* and *Euphorbia coralli-
oides*, whereas lack of management might be given as the reason
for the disappearance of *Ranunculus ophioglossifolius*: its localities
now being maintained by artificial disturbance of the surface of
the mud at the bottom of the small ponds in which it grows.
Finally there is a group of eight species for which no cause of
decline is known or for which the cause is probably a natural
'biological' one. Two are orchids, *Orchis militaris* and *O. simia*.
For the latter species Wilks (1966) has demonstrated how lack of
pollinators was a major cause of the small size of the population in
a Kent locality. *Spartina alterniflora* originally an introduction,

subsequently declined in Southampton Water following competition with the hybrid *S.* x *anglica* of which it was one of the parents.

4. *Rapidly declining species.* In addition to these 34 rare species which have been reduced to one or two squares in recent years, there are some others which, whilst still occurring in more than two squares, have nevertheless declined so rapidly as to give cause for concern. Table III is a list of all species which had more than 20 squares before 1900 but have less than 10 at the present day. Again they are arranged in groups according to the main most likely cause of decline. Of the 20 species in this class, the decline of 14 is almost certainly due to agriculture. 3 species have been affected by changes in scrub and woodland management, and the rest have declined for natural (or unknown) causes.

Summary of causes of decline

In Table IV the causes of extinction or decline of the three groups which have been considered in detail are brought together. The figures emphasise the overwhelming importance of agriculture: for 37 (49%) of the 75 species, this has probably been the main factor in extinction or decline. It is unfortunate that when the legislation setting up Sites of Special Scientific Interest was enacted, change in agricultural practice was excluded from situations requiring a planning application. In many instances a site, containing a nationally rare and declining species, which cannot be given National Nature Reserve status, cannot be adequately protected because the only lesser status which it can be given specifically omits the very force which is most likely to be destructive. In present circumstances, the future of a rare species in this country will depend on whether or not at least one locality is in a nature reserve, and on whether the management it receives maintains the size of the population. Yet only 29 (54%) of the very rare and rapidly declining species in Tables II and III occur in at least one National Nature Reserve or a site affording equivalent protection.

If we consider all the 253 extant species which were studied during the survey, we find that 136 (54%) occur in at least one reserve. However, if we consider the total number of localities of these rare species, the percentage is very much smaller; only 228 (16%) out of a total of 1,425.

Conclusion

If the conservation organisations, both official and voluntary, are to concern themselves with the future of the rarest species in our flora, then there is still an enormous task to be undertaken. If we, as members of the B.S.B.I., *are* concerned about the future of what is about 20% of our native flora, then I feel sure that we have the greatest responsibility in making sure that these conservation organisations know about the localities, and that it is we who must persuade them to take appropriate protective measures.

TABLE IV

Summary of causes of decline

	Arable change	Plough-ing	Drain-age	Habitat destroyed	Collect-ing	For-estry	No. man-agement	Natural causes	Totals
.nctions	1	0	4	4	2	1	0	8	20
y rare	7	6	5	0	5	2	1	8	34
›id decline	3	4	7	0	0	3	0	3	20
als ..	11	10	16	4	7	6	1	19	74

REFERENCES

PERRING, F. H. and WALTERS, S. M. (1962). *Atlas of the British Flora*. London & Edinburgh.

WILKS, H. M. (1966). The monkey orchid in East Kent. *Handbk Soc. Promot. Nat. Reserves*, 79-80.

DISCUSSION

Mr J. E. LOUSLEY said that whilst the exercise had been valuable there were many ways in which it could be improved. Table I includes several maritime species the populations of which had been fluctuating for centuries. From his own experience he was certain that the destruction of *Spiranthes aestivalis* was entirely due to drainage. Collecting was deplorable but did not contribute to the final loss of this species. He also doubted whether collecting had caused the decline of *Gentiana nivalis* or *Lychnis alpina* which are both very abundant in their extant localities. Some of the data included in Table II needed further analysis: some old records certainly originated in mis-identifications.

Dr PERRING replied that he had issued these admittedly unfinished lists to invite comments from members: he hoped all with additional information would supply it. He added that whilst extant populations of *Gentiana* and *Lychnis* may be thriving some localities have been lost and this has been attributed to over-collecting by correspondents.

Prof. D. A. VALENTINE asked whether habitat data are available for the rare species records.

Dr PERRING replied that this is the next stage of the survey. Observers are being asked to complete a form for each site: habitat details were requested.

Mr C. J. CADBURY asked whether *Matthiola sinuata* was really disappearing from its native sand-dune habitats. It was a species which seemed to benefit from the increasing disturbance which it is receiving at Braunton Burrows. *Corynephorus* was also increasing in some coastal localities: presumably some of the old localities from which it had now gone were on inland heaths.

Dr PERRING confirmed that *Corynephorus* had been lost to ploughing from inland heath sites. The decline of *Matthiola* began before the present pressure on our sand-dunes had built up.

Dr D.P. YOUNG commented on the great difficulties of judging the national picture from local happenings. *Rhinanthus serotinus* had recently increased in Surrey: no-one was certain whether this was an old overlooked locality in which the species had suddenly become more abundant, whether it was an introduction due to horses or a recent mutation.

THE NEXT TWENTY-FIVE YEARS

S. M. WALTERS

Botany School, Cambridge

Introduction

There is something peculiarly appropriate in asking a middle-aged member of the Botanical Society to conclude this conference by speaking on 'the next 25 years'. Given my Biblical 'three score years and ten' I have a fair chance of seeing most of the changes I am tentatively about to predict—and, of course, you have a good chance of pointing out how wrong I am proving to be! It is, in fact, much easier to predict the future than to report objectively the present and the past. To that extent I am very grateful that the task of reporting has been carried out by Dr. Perring and that I am here as the prophet.

There are three topics which I wish to discuss: the future of the British flora, the future of the British countryside, and the future activities of this Society.

The future of the British flora

However much we may deplore the spread of bricks and concrete, mechanised agriculture and motorways, we should remember that *judged purely in terms of floristic richness* the activities of this frenzied society of ours in the British countryside as a whole are still, on balance, increasing the interest of the British flora rather than decreasing it. Let me illustrate this with one or two examples. In compiling statistics for *A Flora of Cambridgeshire* (Perring *et al.* 1964) on a 10 km square basis, we found that by far the 'richest' square, in number of vascular plants, was the one including the City of Cambridge; and even when you have made due allowance for two complicating factors, namely that there are (and have been) far more competent botanists looking at plants in Cambridge City than in most other squares in the County, and that Cambridge City records go back three centuries, so that the total recorded flora includes many plants not recently seen, it is still true that a more or less urbanised 10 km square is likely to have the longest species list.

As Lousley (p. 73) has shown, modern transport enables us to bring into Britain, consciously or unconsciously, a surprisingly large sample of the world's flora, and experiments in naturalisation are actually going on before our eyes all the time. Most of them are unplanned experiments, but if we watch we can learn a great deal from them. I should like to return to this point later. For the present, I can perhaps illustrate my point best by saying that, if I walk into the centre of Cambridge from the Herbarium tomorrow,

I am likely to see three conspicuous weeds, *Conyza canadensis*, *Epilobium adenocaulon* and *Senecio squalidus*: not one of these weeds was known to my predecessor, Professor Babington, as a Cambridgeshire plant, when he compiled his Cambridgeshire Flora in 1860. Indeed, the spread of one of them has occurred literally 'before my eyes': as an undergraduate I knew only *Epilobium roseum* as a street weed where now the American alien *E. adenocaulon* is by far the commonest Willowherb.

The fact is that man's varied activities continue to produce temporary open habitats all around us, and our efficient transport system provides, directly or indirectly, a source of seed from a wide spectrum of the world's flora. I see no prospect of this situation being radically different within the next quarter-century. Indeed, although for other reasons I would prefer the pace of so-called progress to slacken, in terms of floristic variety the spread of people, houses, factories and motorways can hardly do other than to increase the botanical interest.

Lest you should think I am callously indifferent to the fate of the English countryside, I must now hasten to my second point.

The future of British vegetation and the countryside.

This enormous topic is one in which this Society has been increasingly involved in recent years. At the risk of over-simplifying I wish to avoid the temptation to talk about nature conservation yet again, and try to make a few predictions. In doing this, I lean very heavily on the factual analysis which Dr. Perring has made in recent years for the Nature Conservancy (pps 128-135). Firstly, whatever we do, national and regional extinctions will continue, and probably at an increasing rate. The wholesale elimination of marginal habitats no longer accidentally or consciously preserved make this quite inevitable. There are several reasons why this destruction will proceed. One became brutally apparent during the long and exhausting struggle which, to its lasting credit, this Society conducted in opposition to the Cow Green Reservoir Scheme— namely that no-one can put a cash value on a rare plant or a rare community of plants, and that governments and organisations in power in our society, whether they label themselves politically left or right, seem to require an argument presented in financial terms before they will alter their policy.

A second reason, equally serious, is perhaps not so intractable. Many of us naturalists have learned over the past twenty years that, if we want to preserve for our children and grandchildren the range of communities and species which we ourselves have enjoyed finding and studying, we shall have to be prepared to spend time, effort and money on nature conservation. But many naturalists are also individualists and all of us are selfish in various ways. We *must* get out of our selfishness and think of the community. What kind of flora do we want to hand on to the next generation?

We are the first generation to have the power to consign, by indifference or by greed and insensitivity, a sizeable proportion of our native flora to extinction. How much survives is up to us, collectively, in Local Conservation Trusts, in this Society, in the Committees of the Nature Conservancy or the Local Government Department. How much of our time is it worth? We all have to answer this question. I am not wholly pessimistic for several reasons. First because of the undoubted success of the nature conservation movement in Britain in finding thousands of people who have answered the question as we would want them to answer it. Secondly because I feel (and here I pass from prediction to speculation) that sooner or later we are going to have a post-agricultural revolution which could well liberate from arable cultivation large areas of the earth's surface. Remarkably few authors seem to have speculated in any detail on this theme; one of the few is Nigel Calder, whose recent book *The Environment Game* I commend to you as full of food for thought for botanist and citizen alike. If and when the large-scale synthesis of carbo-hydrate replaces traditional agriculture, the problem of nature conservation will be quite suddenly and dramatically different. We may well find that our creation of nature reserves and protected areas turns out to have been a modern 'Noah's Ark' operation: after the agricultural flood has passed, the new wilderness areas, consciously set aside for the recreation of the urban population, will be re-colonised from the reserves. There is nothing improbable, or even particularly difficult, about re-populating adjacent areas from a nature reserve. On a small scale we did it at Wicken Fen after the last war, when requisitioned arable land was returned to the National Trust. In five years Adventurers' Fen had so effectively returned to the 'wilderness' of reedswamp and open water that, standing in the middle of it, it was difficult to believe it had not been like that for centuries, yet this involved no conscious intro-ductions of vascular plant species at all. This is, of course, a very good reason for trying to hold, in addition to a small number of large reserves, a much larger number of small reserves scattered through the country, a policy which is in any case forced upon the voluntary conservation movement for historical and political reasons.

Whether the post-agricultural revolution falls in the next twenty-five years or not, we must at least face the prospect that a good many native species will be seen by the next generation of botanists only in protected areas where their continued survival is the conscious concern of organised naturalists. Whilst this situation will undoubtedly depress the more extreme individualists amongst us, it will present new and exciting opportunities to the biologist who would enjoy a precise research problem involving careful observation in the field, together with cultivation and experiment in the garden and even the laboratory.

The future of the B.S.B.I.

The post-war history of the Society has been one of growth and activity whether measured in terms of membership, of volume of publication, or of influence in matters of concern to naturalists. I have greatly enjoyed my connexion with it, and like all my generation was enormously stimulated by the enthusiasm and even devotion which many members showed in the collection of distribution data for the *Atlas of the British Flora* and the *Critical Supplement*. Those of us associated with *Flora Europaea* know how enviously some of our continental botanical colleagues look upon the activities of this Society, with its traditional mixture of amateur and professional botanist. A little self-congratulation does not come amiss here.

After the self-congratulation, however, comes the questioning. What is the future of the Society in the next quarter-century? Here I shall abandon prediction, and simply state some things I should like to see it do. These are not necessarily in order of preference and not in any sense meant to be exhaustive; but if the B.S.B.I. manages to cover most of this list, I shall be satisfied.

1. Retain the rather impressive mixture of amateur and professional. The professionals gain from the amateurs a constantly-renewed vision of the zest for the game, and an enormous amount of information. What the amateurs gain from the professionals is perhaps more doubtful, and in any case it would not do for me to say, but it seems to work reciprocally. With the increased leisure and mobility of people, we can expect a steady increase in effective amateur contribution, so long as the Society can find the right ways of eliciting the response.

2. Be more concerned about quality of activity, than growth in numbers, which is far less important.

3. Take much more seriously still responsibility in the botanical aspects of nature conservation. As one of the sponsoring organisations of the Wild Plant Protection Working Party, as an advisor on botanical matters to the Nature Conservancy, as a responsible Society member of the Council for Nature, and in many other ways, the B.S.B.I. can do much in the next twenty-five years. European Conservation Year, 1970, is the time to renew our resolution. A particular concern could be shown by the Society about the future of those plant species (not necessarily among the rarest species *in Britain*) for which we probably or certainly hold the largest surviving populations. If we can list, as a by-product of *Flora Europaea*, the thousand-or-so rare or local endemic vascular plants of Europe, I would also hope that the appropriate Society in each European country might be encouraged to take a particular interest in the conservation of a selected group of plants taken from the main list. We hope to make a modest beginning with the main list in 1970.

4. Encourage, perhaps jointly with the British Ecological Society, the study of rare or local plant species in nature reserves and protected areas. Our knowledge of the autecology of rare species is pathetically inadequate, and such studies

are ideally suited to amateur investigation. I should like to see the Conservation Committee of the Society taking an active interest in this field. We shall soon know where many of our rare species are and in a good many cases how big the remaining populations are; can we in the next decade make a drive to find out enough about them to be able to protect them from subtle ecological changes which would cause their extinction? To make members responsible for the study of rare or local species which they are involved in protecting would seem to be an ideal way of educating the next generation of field botanists. County Naturalists' Trusts have made a good start in this field; perhaps the Society can give more formal help.

5. Develop the network research type of project, so that members continue to feel that they can individually contribute to a joint, cooperative project of scientific interest and value. The *Symphytum* and *Silene vulgaris* surveys are admirable examples of the kind of recording which the Society's structure makes possible.

6. Take up Mr. Fryer's excellent suggestion (p. 116) and make a special effort to study the weed and ruderal flora of Britain, both in traditional ways which the Society has always encouraged (recording of rare aliens on waste ground, etc.) and in terms of more detailed surveys of ruderal floras over a period of years. Many of the most rapid changes (such as the replacement of native *Epilobium* weeds by the alien *E. adenocaulon* already mentioned) are of great ecological and microevolutionary importance, and careful and consistent recording would be enormously valuable.

7. Initiate one or two common species surveys to provide opportunities for all members, young and old, city and country, to contribute something. This would be particularly fruitful where a little research has revealed the outline of an interesting problem, and the mass collection of simple data is needed. This is a matter mainly for the professionals, especially the experimental taxonomists interested in variation, to advise and plan. Suitable subjects are certainly available, arising in some cases (e.g. *Centaurea nigra*) from papers published in the Society's journals. Here Dr. Mellanby's suggestion (p. 101) of the ecotypic selection of common species to tolerate contamination is very relevant.

8. Using the excellent *British Sedges* (Jermy and Tutin 1968) as a model, expand the publication of such works, which have both a permanent scientific value and an amateur appeal. Several other difficult groups are eminently suitable subjects.

9. Retain the important tradition of the Conference on some general theme. The Society is increasingly known professionally by the published results of its Conferences.

10. Finally, remember that what holds the Society together is *enthusiasm for the game*. Avoid a professional class of paid

officials as long as possible, but give the overworked voluntary officers as much office and secretarial help as the Society can possibly afford.

I hope, in conclusion, that the Society might be able to invite me back twenty-five years hence and report that it has done all these things and more!

REFERENCES

BABINGTON, C. C. (1860). *Flora of Cambridgeshire.* London.

CALDER, N. (1966). *The Environment Game.* London.

JERMY, A. C. and TUTIN, T. G. (1968). *British Sedges.* London.

PERRING, F. H., SELL, P. D., WALTERS, S. M. and WHITEHOUSE, H. L. K. (1964). *A Flora of Cambridgeshire.* Cambridge.

DISCUSSION

Mr M. G. SCHULTZ asked what sort of energy Calder suggests would be used instead of carbohydrates in the post-agricultural revolution.

Dr K. MELLANBY thought that the large-scale synthesis of carbohydrates would never occur because the process would probably demand more water than could be found by the nation. Nevertheless much land was already out of agricultural production in North America, though he believed it could only be a cyclic phenomenon.

Dr WALTERS argued that whether permanent or cyclic such opportunities for recolonisation were bound to have a profound effect on our attitude to nature reserve management.

SUMMING-UP

E. MILNE-REDHEAD

President of the B.S.B.I.

We have covered an immense amount of ground since this conference opened yesterday morning, and have heard some interesting facts about, and reasons for, many things which most of us have hitherto taken for granted. We have also heard some alarming prognostications. It was good to hear from Mr. Lamb that botanical information, especially pollen analysis, has played a major part in the present state of our knowledge of past climates. It is terrifying to think that one day man may be deliberately attempting to change climate, with of course untold consequential changes in our fauna and flora!

We have seen from Dr. Savidge how, on one small mountain of relatively uniform topography in Wales, vegetation was controlled largely by aspect and soil. We have compared under the guidance of Prof. Pigott the behaviour of *Cirsium acaule* on the chalk of SE England and on the limestone in Derbyshire, where it is at the edge of its range and have noticed why in the latter locality it is much more particular as to its aspect and is much more reluctant to set good seed. Some plants however at the edge of their range do produce great quantities of seed. I refer to my hobby horse, *Ranunculus ophioglossifolius*, which owes its existence in Britain to-day to the fact that it seeds very abundantly and that the seeds can survive many years of dormancy. But, unlike *Cirsium acaule*, *Ranunculus ophioglossifolius* is an annual and as such is much more dependent on seed production for survival.

The reasons for the changes in agricultural practice, which have had such a harmful effect on our flora, were ably outlined by Mr. Trist who described the dangers of farms run by big business with managers appointed to make money regardless of other considerations. The brighter side is that some farmers are beginning to realise that some degree of conservation is worthwhile; for instance, that it is a waste of money to spray crops solely to destroy relatively harmless weeds such as *Veronica* spp., *Anagallis* and *Kickxia*. I have for long urged the Nature Conservancy to acquire and manage some arable fields in the traditional way, allowing the weeds such as poppy, cornflower, corn-cockle and corn marigold to flourish. I believe such fields would be of considerable interest to many people besides botanists. Mr. Trist deplored the fact that S.S.S.I.s in general have no protection from ploughing and that grants can be obtained for that very purpose. Was it not the height of folly that, a few years ago, the Nature Conservancy was trying to secure Borth Bog as a nature reserve whilst the Ministry of Agriculture was offering a subsidy to make it suitable for growing potatoes? !

Tree planting or rather the formation of plantations as carried out by the Forestry Commission was described by Mr. Brown and it was accepted that much natural vegetation was inevitably being destroyed, especially where the planted trees were conifers. It is a pity that hardwood plantations cannot be established more economically in England. After all, the escarpment beech-woods on the Cotswolds are an artefact, having largely been planted by the landowners after the Napoleonic wars with particularly fine strains of beech obtained from Belgium. These woods are a joy to botanists, and three fine examples are being managed both in the traditional way for timber production and, at the same time, as nature reserves.

Mr. Trist's reference to the destruction of hedgerows in East Anglia was amplified by Dr. Hooper. I hope his prophecies fall far short of the mark! I wonder if he has noticed the mature hedgerows flanking the M4 near Maidenhead which must have been planted by some enlightened planner many years before the construction of the motorway was begun.

Mr. Gray provided some food for thought regarding the colonization of estuaries following barrage building. He must be a brave man to risk predicting what will actually happen!

Mr. Lousley showed how the rise and fall of various forms of transport had affected our flora. There is one method of transport however that Mr. Lousley did not mention; it is the hovercraft. By a narrow margin the Devon County Council has prevented the destruction of part of the National Nature Reserve on Braunton Burrows this summer, but the threat is still on. I hope the National Farmers' Union will unite with the naturalists and conservationists to prevent this happening, as, not only would part of the N.N.R. be destroyed but the valuable farm land behind the Burrows might be turned into desert. Members should be on the lookout for similar attacks elsewhere on coastal dune systems.

Mr. Dunball described the problems of planting trees and shrubs on motorways and outlined the Ministry's policy which I applaud, apart from the use of sycamore, an exotic tree which does so much harm to our native flora, and which I look upon as a tree weed. I wonder if the Landscape Committee of the Ministry of Transport has ever considered making ponds on the acres of ground sterilized by motorway interchanges. These would to some extent compensate for the great loss of ponds resulting from modern farming practice.

The final paper yesterday gave a fascinating account by Dr. Gillham of the various ways in which seed and vegetable matter gets transported by birds. Can birds have been responsible for taking *Utricularia australis*, better known as *U. neglecta*, from Britain to Central Africa and Australia one wonders, or was it Alan Cobham?

Dr. Mellanby this morning reviewed the effects on plants of the use of insecticides in addition to the too well-known results of herbicides, which have disfigured and impoverished so many of our roadside verges. He also analysed the dangers of pollution of our water courses by sewage, effluents, slurrey, detergents etc., which cause an abnormal concentration of nitrates and phosphates with harmful effects on the aquatic flora.

Dr. Fryer discussed the control of weeds in arable land and pasture and threw much light on the relative selectivity of the chemicals used, and the strains of arable weeds which are becoming resistant to herbicides. I was interested to learn that there was evidence that weed species in arable land were seldom eliminated by applications of herbicides but that the population could be reduced to harmless levels.

Dr. Bowen discussed the four principal gaseous contaminants of the atmosphere and pointed out that sulphur dioxide from impurities in both coal and oil fuels was the most harmful to the flora, especially to evergreens and conifers. He suggested that it had probably reduced the incidence of juniper near urban areas. Other contaminants of lesser importance were also mentioned. Luckily most of the rare bryophytes and lichens exist in northern areas relatively free from industrial pollution.

I do not think I need remind you of the two stimulating papers which you have just heard. Dr. Perring's analysis of plants in danger may be criticized in detail and I am sure he will be grateful for any additions and corrections which members care to send him. It does however form a most useful basis for assessing the situation. Dr. Walters produced some terrifying thoughts on what the country-side may be like in 25 years. One can but hope that his predictions do not take place.

Before closing I feel that further mention must be made of the Wild Plant Protection Bill. It is hoped that a modified Bill professionally drafted will be submitted to Parliament during the next session and that European Conservation Year 1970 will see a measure for plant protection on the Statute Book just 100 years after the first measure for the protection of birds.

INDEX

For trees and shrubs both the scientific and the English names are included though the text may only refer to one of these names. For other species the scientific names are included when the text reference is an English name only, but English names are not included for species which are only referred to by their scientific name.

Names of places, other than the more prominent ones, are not included, but may be found by referring to the County in which they occur.